MOSQUITO - 50 YEARS ON

"probably man's highest engineering achievement in timber"

HATFIELD RAeS

A report on the 50th Anniversary Symposium
held at British Aerospace Hatfield
on the 24th November 1990

First Published in 1991
by GMS Enterprises
67 Pyhill Bretton
Peterborough
Tel (0733) 265123

ISBN 1 870384 11 3

Overall Copyright: Hatfield RAeS

Body of text set in Times 10pt
on Apple Mackintosh DTP System

Printed for GMS Enterprises by
Woolnough Limited
Express Works, Church Street
Irthlingborough
Northants
England

CONTENTS

FOREWORD - Page 5
Ralph Hare

THE ORIGINAL CONCEPT - Page 7
Speaker - Michael J Bowyer
Incorporating the opening address
by Lee Balthazor, RAeS Branch Chairman

THE MERLIN ENGINE -Page 17
Speaker - Alec Harvey-Bailey

WOODEN WORK OF ART - Page 31
Speaker - Mike Ramsden

RECOLLECTIONS OF AN APPRENTICE - Page 43
Speaker - Frank Cooper

PRODUCTION - Page 52
Speaker - Frank Vann

TEST FLYING THE EARLY MOSQUITOES - Page 66
Speaker - Pat Fillingham

EVOLUTION - Page 75
Speaker - Michael J Bowyer

OPERATIONS OF MOSQUITO NIGHT FIGHTERS - Page 86
Speaker - Group Captain John Cunningham

DECK LANDING OF FIRST TWIN ENGINED AIRCRAFT - Page 94
Speaker - Captain Eric Brown

OPERATIONS OF 617 SQUADRON - Page 105
Speaker - Jim Shortland

HISTORICAL PERSPECTIVE - Page 114
Speaker - Mike Ramsden

AFTER DINNER THOUGHTS - Page 117

25TH NOVEMBER 1990 - Page 128
Ian Thirsk - De Havilland Aircraft Museum

COME ON DOWN! THE STORY OF FLYING TO THE SYMPOSIUM - Page 138
John Sadler - Pilot of BAe Mosquito RR299

PUBLISHERS NOTE

This title has been produced from the transcription of some nine hours of raw, un-edited tape recordings which were recorded 'as it happened' at Hatfield on Saturday November 24th 1991 - the day of the Mosquito 50th Anniversary symposium. A certain amount of 'editing' of the words spoken that day has been undertaken to both improve the flow of the written, not spoken words and to remove pauses, uncertainties and verbal trip-ups!

Due to the historical importance of the occasion, great care has been taken to use the words spoken that day as the base for this document - use of lecturers notes (where provided) has only been used as 'back-up' to check any unclear items. All the transcriptions have been checked and approved by both the speakers concerned and members of the Hatfield RAeS that were present on the day.

Each speaker was followed by a period of questions and answers. Where a questioner identified themselves, their name is mentioned alongside their question. Where a questioner is not identified, it is because they never identified themselves on the tapes on the day.

The location and amount of illustrative material may vary slightly in position within the printed text of the lecture against where it was presented on the day. This has been undertaken to allow the illustration to fit in with the printed word and to fit in with the restricted amount of space available.

FOREWORD

The commemoration of the 50th Anniversary of the Mosquito's first flight with a symposium has highlighted the history of one of the most remarkable Second World War aircraft. The lecturers in toto have covered the story of design, production, flight-testing and operations quite fully in an interesting way and have done justice to the subject. To those involved, nostalgic sentiments are stirred in the reading of this material.

The flair and resolve of Sir Geoffrey de Havilland, then affectionately known by all as 'Capt. D.H.' ensured the start of the 'bomber with fighter speed' project in spite of much opposition from both official and unofficial doubters.

Led by Mr R. E. Bishop, a brilliant design engineer, a relatively small team produced in about nine months from contract date the prototype aircraft W4050, which first flew in the capable hands of of Geoffrey de Havilland Jnr on the 25th November 1940. However, preliminary work had been unofficially progressing since October 1939. Included in this team were Messrs Clarkson (Aerodynamic wizardry) Wilkins (Fuselage design) and Tamblin (Wing Design). Fred Plumb was in charge of the constructional work.

Long before handling and performance estimates had been confirmed by flight-testing, demands for the supply of other versions were being made - and were soon forthcoming!. The Mosquito was proven to be an extremely versitile aircraft - there was scarcely an air-war role which it did not perform - and usually it out-performed the competition!. The aircraft was very much sought after by RAF Station Commanders and by most Allied Air Forces. The 'Wooden Wonder' was easy to build, to modify, to repair and to maintain. It won much praise from flight and ground-crews alike.

The lectures, discussions and anecdotes contained within these proceedings re-enliven interest in an unique aircraft and in the many personnel associated with it. They form a further tribute to the foresight, technical know-how, competative flair and determination-to-succeed of a number of individuals brought together under the emergencies of total war. These attributes are amongst those which ensure the success of any major enterprise.

The RAeS Hatfield Branch Committee (with the very active support of the de Havilland Aircraft Museum at Salisbury Hall) are to be congratulated on the planning and execution of a most successful symposium.

The announcement of the R E Bishop memorial Award, to interest schoolchildren in aeronautical engineering made at this sympoisum, is particularly appropriate, bearing in mind the interest that R E Bishop had always taken in the D.H. Aeronautical Technical School and its output of qualified students.

Ralph Hare

Ralph Hare.
November 1991

ACKNOWLEDGEMENTS

The Hatfield Branch of the Royal Aeronautical Society acknowledge their thanks to John Edwards, Keith Miles, Rex Nichamin and John Sauders for organising the Symposium. They would also like to acknowledge the support given by British Aerospace (Commercial Aircraft) Limited, Rolls Royce and the Mosquito Aircraft Museum.

Special mention must be made to Madelaine Butt for many hours spent transcribing the tapes of the occasion and to Darryl Cott for locating and providing many of the photographs.

Thanks must also be expressed to all of the speakers and to Allan Lupton and Graham Simons for their efforts in the production and publication these proceedings.

Lee Balthazor
Chairman, Hatfield RAeS
November 1991

CHAPTER ONE

THE ORIGINAL CONCEPT
Speaker - Michael J Bowyer

The Opening Address of the Symposium was given by Mr. Lee R. Balthazor - Chairman Hatfield Branch of the Royal Aeronautical Society and SVP 146 Project.

"It is a privilege and an honour to welcome everyone on behalf of the Hatfield Branch of the Royal Aeronautical Society to this historic occasion on the 50th Anniversary of the first flight of the Mosquito.

What we have planned for today is a programme which is quite intensive and we hope that during the course of the day there will be opportunities for all of you who want to contribute to do so.

This particular occasion also happens to be quite significant as far as the Branch is concerned, for today is also an appropriate time I think to launch the R. E. Bishop Memorial Award. This award has been organised by the Hatfield Branch of the Royal Aeronautical Society and sponsored jointly by British Aerospace Hatfield, the local Branch and the Royal Aeronautical Society. We decided that a fitting memorial to such an aircraft designer as Ronald Bishop would be a fund which would encourage school children to have an interest in Aerospace; to be encouraged into Engineering, Science and Technology, and to understand and participate in what team-work is all about. Therefore a lot of the activity today will be generating revenue for the R. E. Bishop memorial award and we hope that this, with the sponsorship from the Society and British Aerospace, will enable us to establish a fund to launch a prototype scheme in the local schools in the local area and we do believe that this will take off and become perhaps a regional and even a national activity."

Lee Balthazor then handed over to Charles Masefield - President of the Royal Aeronautical Society Hatfield Branch and Managing Director of the Airlines Division, British Aerospace.

"Good Morning Ladies and Gentlemen, and thank you Lee. Kicking off the batting this morning is Michael Bowyer whom, as you know, is not only a well-known aviation historian, but also visited Hatfield and de Havilland during the days and months prior to the start of the book 'Mosquito' so he is going to set the scene for us this morning, talking about the origins of the aircraft's concept.

Michael was saying to me earlier this morning that he always used to feel that when people worked at de Havilland they were not working for a Company in those days, they were working for a concept - which was a thought I rather liked. He is going to talk about not only the origins of the concept but the activities that were taking place prior to the start of the design and development. So Michael, over to you."

Michael Bowyer took the podium.

"Mr President, Ladies and Gentlemen. I am conscious standing here that I am addressing you at the end of a very remarkable week in British history and talking about a very remarkable aeroplane - which I remember throughout much of its career and had dealings with in the RAF at the end of its career. I am also going to stand here during the day and, like many of you, I shall be thinking of the people I served with in the RAF and of those that I came to know when, with Martin Sharp, I wrote the book 'Mosquito'. I know many of you will have friends who served on Mossies, so this is a rather nice get together on a very special day in British aviation history.

I think the word remarkable has to be applied to the Mosquito. It was the world's first multi-role combat aircraft - of that there is no question, for very few fighters turn into airliners or torpedo bombers at the same time as they bomb Berlin with impunity twice a night and carry a 4,000 pounder in the process. It was a remarkable concept.

In October 1934 the MacRobertson Air Race took place from Mildenhall, where we had seen an amazing aeroplane - the DH88 Comet Racer (Fig.1). This was a little aeroplane with no military application, but had within it the germ, the kernel of what was to become the Mosquito. Three weeks after that air race had been won in 71 hours (which must have seemed incredible to everybody who took part - I know at the time I thought this is unbelievable that an aeroplane can get to Australia in such a short time) the Company was looking towards the possibility of an airliner based upon the Comet racer, and they began work on what was to become the the DH91 Albatross (Fig 2).

Fig 1: The aircraft that started it all - the famous DH88 'Comet Racer' that won the 1934 Mildenhall to Melbourne Air Race. (Photo:BAe)

Fig 2: The DH91 Albatross - an all wooden construction airliner, powered by four Gipsy Twelve inverted Vee-12 engines. De Havilland made a number of studies relating to the possibility of turning this into a potent military machine. (Photo: BAe)

Of course, it was difficult getting funding for such an aeroplane from the Government, and the Company had to do their best with the resources available, for they were entering what was a different market away from small aeroplanes. They looked at the possibility of an aircraft for the North Atlantic route, carrying a 1,000lb payload with a 2,500 mile sector range and able to cruise at around 210mph. They also did forecasts for an aeroplane carrying a 6,000lb load to Berlin - a matter of 1,200 miles, flying at something like 11,000ft.

At the same time the government had set on course two large bomber programmes; B12/36, which was to lead to the heavily armed Short Stirling that was intended to fight its way through to distant targets and P13/36, which created the smaller Avro Manchester. They issued this latter specification which called for a twin-engined medium bomber for world-wide use, an aircraft which could exploit the alternatives between long range and a very heavy bomb load made possible by novel launching methods. The highest possible cruising speed was necessary and nose and tail gun turrets were essential. Bombs could perhaps be carried in tiers. 'It appears,' it said, 'that there is a possibility of combining a medium bomber general reconnaissance and general purposes aircraft in one design, with a top speed of 275mph at 15,000ft.'

The Company wondered whether a Military Albatross was a possible answer. Speed through aerodynamic cleanness, minimum skin area and, if possible, more powerful in-line engines that were coming along - was it possible to adapt this Military Albatross to a specification that eventually led to the Manchester and finally to the Lancaster?. They drew up estimates in 1938 for a twin Merlin design, another variation with two Hercules engines and the third with the spectacular (or thought to be spectacular) Napier Sabre.

During the summer of 1938 they considered how they could go about developing the Albatross, and in July wrote to the Air Council through Sir Wilfrid Freeman who was the Member for Research and Development. In their letter they discussed the specification of the aircraft and argued for wood. Wood, they said, '...is as strong in all but torsion as metal which was being introduced in so many aircraft particularly on the other side of the Atlantic'. They suggested a different approach though to the specification. Later that month they decided it was not possible that a twin-engined Albatross could meet all the requirements - if you had the speed you would carry half the load, if you carried the full load you would have a larger aircraft which inevitably must be slower. They reckoned that they would have a 1,500 mile range for a 4,000lb load, the aircraft would cruise at 230-240mph at 18,000ft.

When I was doing work for 'Mosquito', I came across a letter from the Company that said 'a good bomber could be produced using Merlins'. This we thought was the first twinkle of the idea that became the Mosquito, but to meet this specification, double the power would be needed. A compromise bomber might be considered if some of the Appendix A stuff - that's all the little bits and pieces, such as the exotic sun helmets or pith helmets which many British bombers were supposed to carry - were dispensed with, the speed asked for reduced, and height of operation increased. A two-Merlin compromise bomber could be arrived at and, indeed, in August of that year they drew up plans for it. They decided that speed and not defence would be essential and that the aircraft should not be an adaptation of the Albatross. It should be much smaller than they had earlier envisaged, probably with a crew of two and a pair of Merlins.

Then of course came the Munich crisis. They decided that it was obvious that war was coming and they must visit the Air Ministry personally to discuss their schemes - no more letter writing. So Captain de Havilland and Charles Walker went along and discussed with the Ministry the possibility of a wooden aeroplane - 'the Comet was wood' they said, 'the Albatross would be wood. Wood was a good thing - it would save a year in the development phase and, also in war time, employ furniture makers and similar people'. You could, as it were, stick it together, small firms could be involved, there was every advantage in doing that - you did not need a factory as such!. But that was a radical idea and already the die had been cast for the big bombers, the trend was towards metal aircraft and also towards four engines.

They were told to go away and make some other plans for helping the potential war effort. Maybe making wings - make more trainers which they appeared to be quite good at. I remember when we began the book, Sir Geoffrey de Havilland turned to Martin Sharp (I was standing nearby and was not then talking to him) and he said "in life you must never give up". He turned and looked at me -I thought 'goodness I think he really means me!', so I decided I'd better never give up in life, for others had not decided to give up!.

Behind the scenes of course there was another deep concern, the worry over the Blenheim. When de Havilland put forward an idea for 'a bomber with fighter speed' which was a lovely phrase to describe the Mosquito - the RAF had already had one of those and that was the Blenheim. Unfortunately the fighters were biplane fighters and it was going to face monoplane fighters with more speed than the Blenheim possessed. This bomber from de Havilland would have to achieve 300mph (that's minimum speed) and by October 1938 the idea was perhaps that a crew of three would be necessary, maybe a tail turret, possibly forward guns for ground strafing. Its weight would be about 19,000 lb, it would be made of wood and the wingspan would be about 61ft. That was still quite a sizeable aeroplane and if it achieved 300mph, then it wasn't going to achieve a lot more!.

Then of course the Company was making the Flamingo (Fig.3), a very elegant looking metal aeroplane, which again was a break-away. It was able to carry between 12 and 20

Fig.3: de Havilland's all-metal DH95 Flamingo - later to appear in limited RAF service as the 'Hertfordshire' with only one machine being built as such. (The remainder that were used by the RAF were impressed civilian examples). This design was about the size of aircraft they were considering, but the machine placed unacceptable demands on the metal industry. (Photo: BAe)

people, about the size of the aeroplane they had just been thinking of as a bomber. They decided to work upon a project based upon the Flamingo that would have a nosewheel undercarriage which then was very revolutionary. The design would carry four 500 pounders, but all these aeroplanes were not revolutionary, they were advances of what was already in being.

By 1939 the Company was still looking for the concept of a useful bomber and gradually they concluded that the one thing that spoiled many bombers was the fact that they carried an enormous amount of weight in mere defensive armament. If you got rid of the defensive guns and the turrets (which weigh a terrific amount) then one sixth of the total weight had been relieved. Did they do any good? Well, they defended the aircraft getting there and back, but they didn't actually improve the bombing accuracy. They didn't improve the offensive capability or anything like that, they could not stop anti-aircraft guns firing at the aircraft and they were a threat. Therefore, it was obvious that the guns should go - speed seemed to be the number one essential.

Number two was the ability to fly quite high, and of course in those days flying high was the main aim of the bomber force and for protection. The importance of the word 'height' (which was perhaps better than just thinking of altitude) was that you could fly low as well, you could fly above the anti-aircraft guns, you could fly below even the medium anti-aircraft guns operating below about 11,000ft and of course manoeuvrability would be essential, for if you were being chased you would have to have a manoeuvrable aircraft to get away.

They began to argue that a small aeroplane would take less time to build, it wouldn't cost so much, it would be easier to service, and of course it would be easier to teach people to fly it - you wouldn't need a team, you would need a pilot. Training those people would be very expensive, particularly in war time, if losses accrued rapidly. So the move came towards an aeroplane which could make more flights in a given time and that could still carry a good bomb load. When these ideas were put to the Ministry, their answer was 'Yes but, supposing your estimates are wrong?. You're talking of a differential between fighters and bombers of maybe a few miles per hour, what if the enemy has a faster fighter - look what has happened to the Blenheim!'.

Well, then came the war, and those who were working on the Albatross (and the Albatross was still in production here) found that their talents should be put elsewhere. Four days after war began, the company team went again to the Ministry and said 'look, we have thought all this out, these are our new ideas - we are convinced'. They found the Ministry less sceptical, 'Would it really be faster?, could two men cope with all the work, and you tell us that while we have Wellingtons that are finding it difficult to get to Brunsbüttel and back, you are telling us that Berlin for you is two hours away - and you're going there in impunity?'.

It's easy to talk with hindsight isn't it?. All day long we are going to be talking with hindsight, but if you had to send people into action in an aeroplane, the sort of aeroplane that might not be fast enough, one probably would think long before making the decision, and so much was involved. They said 'Make some new estimates, have you thought of the Rolls Royce Griffon?. As we all know the Rolls Royce Griffon - either the first Griffon or the second version - was a long way away.

It seemed to the Company that the Merlin would probably be the best bet - it was at the beginning of its life and had enormous development potential as I am sure we are going to hear about today. They looked at another quixotic engine that the Ministry appeared to want to foist on every British aeroplane manufacturer - the Napier Dagger. In the end the Hereford had to suffer it, the Stirling was intended to have the Dagger, even the Spitfire was intended to have the Dagger. Surely here is a chance for the Mosquito; that too can have the Dagger. What would happen if there were one Sabre fitted?, Somebody else had already thought of that, because while de Havilland were doing their unarmed bomber, then Short Brothers also had a very exotic aeroplane on the drawing board. It was based on the Mercury 'Maia' Mail Carrier and a small aeroplane without an undercarriage and landing on skids when it got back. It could go very fast, fly quite high, bomb the target, be launched once the carrier was airborne... It was quite a remarkable idea, but of course having lots of launch aircraft, having to line then up on the airfield, all very vulnerable with many complications... The idea died. No, it was no good going for such things.

The effect of wing thickness variations was then considered. Drag was re-examined. Would the de Havilland aeroplane be able to get much from exhaust propulsion?. What was the effect of adding armament?. What about a two gun turret?. That's 500lb., it would take 20mph off; no way. On October 16th 1939, the cost of the two-gun power turret, with a third crew member and one traversing gun perhaps was worked out. Whatever way they looked there was no doubt about it - the unarmed bomber was the thing to stand for.

So in late November 1939, they went to meet Sir Wilfrid Freeman to discuss all their findings of the last few weeks. Captain de Havilland attended and Charles Walker went, and they strongly pressed the argument against any armament. 'Speed,' they said 'would be

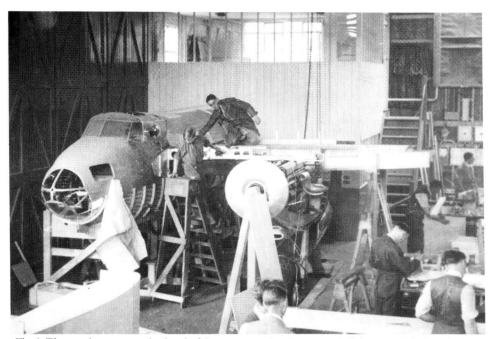

Fig.4: The mock-up proceeds ahead of the prototype in a hangar at Salisbury Hall during the first half of 1940. The view from the cockpit over the engines was considered important, and the value of a side blister to improve the view aft is being considered in this picture. A Merlin is installed in the port engine position, supported by timber baulks. (Photo: BAe)

obtained without it, and most interceptions could be avoided'. 'What would its speed be?'. They thought about 397mph. In fact, when the Mosquitoes went into action with 105 Squadron they could obtain about 380-388 in theory, if all was well. So the estimates in fact, were pretty accurate. Nobody now wanted a compromise aeroplane. The Ministry said 'If we go ahead with the aircraft, is it just going to be an unarmed bomber or can it do anything else?'. Well, possibly, and when R. E. Bishop did the drawings for the aeroplane he made sure that there would be room under the cockpit in the fuselage for guns. If there was no bomb aimer's position in the nose, then guns could be fitted in the nose, and immediately the aircraft had become what we now would call a strike fighter. So here was a three-man maybe a two-man bomber which now had the potential of being a very fast fighter, faster in fact than the Spitfire of its day.

In early December there was a major conference to discuss the whole idea. The compromise armed bomber was out of favour, but Bomber Command said 'We have no place for these machines, they don't fit in the concept that we have of a bombing programme'. Sir Wilfrid Freeman championed the cause and a decision was eventually made to order a prototype, supported by a mock-up (Fig.4), but it went ahead not as the unarmed bomber. That prototype would be an unarmed reconnaissance aircraft and it was really as a reconnaissance aeroplane that the Mosquito made its entry into service.

On 1 March 1940, 50 Mosquitoes were ordered, but most of those strangely enough were not to be bombers. They were to replace the Blenheim in the reconnaissance role.

Well, in the time available I hope I have sketched in the origins of the Mosquito, and now we will have a few minutes for questions and discussion.'

Discussion

Charles Masefield then returned to the podium:

"Thank you very much Michael for a marvellous scene setting and how remarkable that perhaps the least compromising aircraft ever designed started off as a discussion about how best to compromise. Now can we just have one or two questions that we just have time for or even comments. Who is going to open the bowling?".

At this point those gathered demonstrated a marked reluctance to asking questions, which caused Mr Masefield to suggest: "As the day moves on we will be flooded!".

From the floor: "What was the Mosquito like to fly?".

Charles Masefield: "Well I think that we are going to have later on in the day some talks by some very distinguished Mosquito pilots, who both were involved in the test flying and the actual operational flying, so I think perhaps that question would be best left to those sessions".

David Newman: "At this part of the proceedings it might be interesting to recall that there was a great deal of disbelief about our drag estimates and I can remember spending a Sunday at Salisbury Hall writing out in words of not more than two syllables for the benefit of the Ministry, a detailed analysis of the known and measured drag of the Albatross and an estimate of the drag of the Mosquito using the same methods and comparable detail. As I understand it they had to have that before they were convinced that we were talking sensible numbers about our drag estimate".

Michael Bowyer. "I think also that they were not too happy at the performance of the de Havilland Don the multi-role trainer at the time. The Ministry compared de Havilland's drag estimates of that with the performance of the aircraft, which was perhaps a little unfortunate".

Peter Stokes: " The Westland Whirlwind, there always appeared to be a relationship wing-wise, engine nacelles etc, true or false?".

Michael Bowyer: "That is a mammoth question to ask!. I've always thought that myself, I think in reality there was no comparison. The problem with the Whirlwind was the fuselage was too small. I think that summed it up, a very clever design wasn't it?".

David Boddington, Editor Radio Control Scale Aircraft: "I have read in the past about the Mosquito where people have said that we could have had it two or three years earlier than we did. Now nothing you have said today suggests that fact. Would you like to comment on that please?".

Michael Bowyer: "I suppose again that's a highly complex question, I would have thought we could have had it a year earlier, that assumes that the engines were available, and I remember when we launched the Mosquito book, Sir Peter Wykeham who was then Vice Chief of Air Staff (Training) went to a RAeS meeting, and stood up and said 'Well I have been looking at some files and my feeling is one of the reasons why the Mosquito didn't go forward was that there weren't sufficient Merlin engines'. It wasn't just a simple matter of saying that the aircraft won't do the job, it is a highly complex business at all times, but I would have thought that it could have been in service a lot sooner, and certainly as a bomber. So a year maybe. Had it been in service a year sooner it is interesting to think what effect it would have had on the Battle of Britain".

Charles Masefield: "I think that one thing that hasn't changed in the last 50 years is that one of the most difficult aspects to giving birth to any new programme is making the bureaucrats understand the importance of doing it".

Michael Bowyer: "I am sure you're right there".

Wilf Bishop: "I am particularly interested in the structural concepts, was there evidence of considerable scepticism about such a unique and unusual concept as a lightweight wooden sandwich structure at the time?. Also, having to try to sell the concept of speed and the design concept on top of a unique new structural one, didn't that make it difficult or...?

Michael Bowyer: "I never came across any correspondence or anything when I researched for the book at Hatfield to suggest that, but I think maybe that side of it was a good way in the future from the concept. I don't know whether others who are talking today can tell you more about that side, but my impression of it was that, no, that didn't come into the argument at all. I don't think they were exactly against an aeroplane being made of wood either, you see they were gearing up for an air force that had metal aeroplanes, and you have another complication there haven't you?. Talking of the wood construction though, I did love a story that was told to me when I was writing the book, that in Malta they got the local undertaker to repair Mosquitoes. He came along one day and said 'If I am going to have to do this blankety blank job then I am going to do it in style' and he screwed some coffin handles on a real Mosquito".

John Maynard: "Sir Wilfrid Freeman was of course renowned for his support and all that he did for the eight-gun fighter, do I understand from your comments that he was equally supportive of the Mosquito and perhaps a lone voice in the Air Ministry in that connection too?."

Michael Bowyer: "Absolutely so, oh yes, he backed it to the hilt. Of course he was then member for Research and development on the Air Council and he was a very foreseeing person. I think that we owe a lot to him, we hear of some of the others who backed the eight-gun fighter but there were other people in the Air Force less well known by name perhaps and associations and so on and who did a lot for those projects and certainly he did. Most definitely so, and of course during the middle of the war he was quite keen on developing the concept of an unarmed bomber leading possibly to a four-engined unarmed bomber and through the later de Havilland ideas. Yes indeed".

Charles Masefield: "I think just one final question."

From the floor: "What height was the maximum speed estimate taken?"

Michael Bowyer: "22,000ft. That was the height at which the Mosquito operated in the first instance. When they did the Cologne raid after the famous thousand bomber raid, by chance one person decided that there was scope to go in much lower and when he did go lower then a completely new world was opened. Because he was virtually going under the radar we might say 'in 'Buccaneer' style of later years'. The Mosquito in nearly every way was a pace setter, not perhaps always by intent but often due to skill and by good fortune perhaps".

Charles Masefield: "Well Michael, thank you very much for that splendid scene setting start to the day and for generating the atmosphere that is already building. Now, as you said, a key to the Mosquito's success was the Merlin engine and no aircraft would be an outstanding aircraft unless it is a combination of an outstanding airframe and an outstanding engine."

CHAPTER TWO

THE MERLIN ENGINE
Speaker - Alec Harvey Bailey

This section started with Charles Masefield in the chair: "So to set the scene on that latter half of this partnership we have Mr. Alec Harvey-Bailey who was an Executive with Rolls Royce at the time of the Merlin engine and he is going to describe to us that engine, its concept and background".

Alec Harvey-Bailey took the podium:
"I am sorry to be sitting down but I am slightly walking wounded. Just before I get into this, I could perhaps answer a question about availability of Merlin engines. In 1938 at the time of Munich, 1,700 Merlins had been delivered and I think less than 700 were in aircraft. The first sod was cut at Crewe in May 1938 and by the start of the Battle of Britain 2,000 Merlins had been delivered from that factory.

It is an honour to be asked to make a contribution on the Rolls Royce Merlin on the occasion of the 50th Anniversary of the first flight of the Mosquito.

It was an aircraft covering the whole spectrum of operations with many Mark Numbers and for the sake of simplicity I have decided to break the variants into two classes: those with engines having single stage superchargers and later types with two stage supercharging and intercooling. In Fig 5 we have one of the later types and you will see the

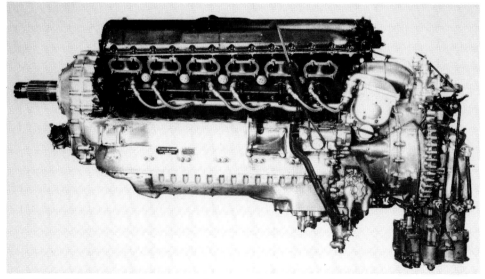

Fig.5: The Merlin 21 - the basic single stage supercharged engine for the Mosquito. It is shown with normal side coolant pipes for production test purposes. (Photo: Rolls Royce)

intercooler intakes just below the spinners and that identifies them.

There is one difference between engines for the Mosquito and those for other aircraft types which saw squadron service, this lies in the cooling system. Normally the main coolant pump, with a flow of about 125 gallons per minute, drew coolant from the radiator, pumping it into the cylinder blocks;from the cylinder head outlets it passed to the header tank and thence to the radiator to complete the circuit. On the Mosquito with its relatively high-set leading edge coolers, coolant was drawn from the header tank by the pump and fed to the radiator via the pump outlets which normally supplied the cylinders. Coolant from the radiator was fed back through a split connection direct to the cylinders. The changes in the engine coolant pipes to accommodate this system, led to Mosquito engines having a different Mark Number from other similar engines. On two stage engines there was also a Mark Number change to identify those engines with cabin blower drive crank-cases for pressurised aircraft. Although the basic 60° V12 single overhead cam layout of 27 litres did not change, the Merlin was subject to progressive redesign to increase power output and at the same time improve reliability.

By the time the first Mosquito flew on the 25th November 1940, the new central entry supercharger devised by Sir Stanley Hooker and Geoffrey Wild was in production. It enabled more advantage to be taken of hundred octane fuel. The two speed supercharged Merlin 21 gave 1,285hp at 3,000 rpm, 12 lbs boost in MS (Moderate Speed) Gear at lower altitudes and in FS (Full Speed) Gear 1,150 at 18,500ft, The 10.25 inch diameter supercharger rotor from the Merlin III had gear ratios of 8.15:1 and 9.49:1, the latter increasing the altitude at which 1,000 hp was available by 5000ft as compared with the Merlin III in the Battle of Britain. The engine featured many product improvement modifications as a result of operational experience, but retained the one-piece cylinder block with detailed improvements to the top joint.

In October 1942 Rolls Royce despatched the first Merlin 23, introducing the two-piece block and allowing boost pressure to be increased to 14lbs in MS Gear and 16lbs in FS Gear. We had occasional trouble with transfer ferrule leaks in the transfer of coolant between the head and the skirt, and just by putting two rubbers at each end of the ferrule it virtually overcame the problem - just a matter of statistics. The other interesting thing of course is using vee grooves as we did later, you dont need a ring that fills the groove, you need the ring to fill the groove at about 85-90% of the groove volume to work properly.

A later modification was to put a taper fillet on the liner to stop occasional liner cracks from under the flange. The dry top joint meant that you could not get gas to coolant or coolant to gas leaks. With the boost pressures I have quoted - 1,460 in MS Gear and 1,440 in the FS Gear. The reason for this discrepancy was that the MS Supercharger clutch was nearing its capacity limit, while 'wind up' in the wheel-case spring drive to the supercharger limited FS Gear boost. In the spring of 1943 Derby delivered the first Merlin 25. This engine had an increased capacity MS clutch and stiffer spring drive. It also featured strengthened connecting rods and the double girder piston, allowing still higher boost pressures. With a maximum boost of 18lbs, 1,635hp was available in MS Gear at low-level and over 1,500hp at 9,000ft giving increased low-level aircraft performance.

RAE Farnborough had been developing power boosting systems and 50 Mk. XIII aircraft were modified with Nitrous Oxide injection, giving a substantial increase in

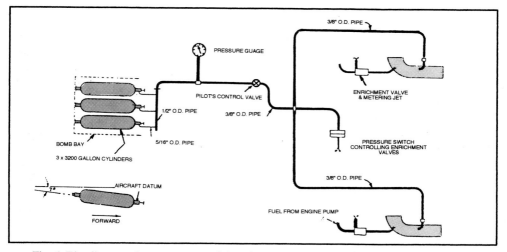

Fig. 6: The diagramatic arrangement of the Nitrous Oxide injection system for the Mosquito Mk.XIII.

performance at altitude. On the night of 2/3 January 1944 John Cunningham flying HK374, a so-modified aircraft shot down an Messerschmitt 410 off Le Touquet and commented favourably on the increased performance.

On the Merlin 23 there would be an increase of about 300hp at 18,000ft, while at 30,000ft close to 1,000hp would be available giving similar performance to the Merlin 61 installed in the Spitfire Mk.IX. The problem with power boosting was the weight and volume of the extra system and the limited time for which it was available. Fig. 6 shows just what extra had to be carried - extra cylinders, pipe systems, control valves and so on. It so happened that the bomb bay on certain marks of Mosquito provided excellent stowage for the gas cylinders, which was not the case in single seat, single-engined fighters. Fig.7 demonstrates just what increase was possible.

The Packard-built single-stage Merlins were fitted to Canadian and Australian-built Mosquitoes and the 225 was the equivalent of the Merlin 25. Packard engines were of similar performance, but differed mechanically in having Bendix Carburettors and an epicyclic supercharger drive in place of the Farman type used on British-built engines. I think that this was because we had some trouble with the Farman drive in the initial stages. It also had quite a number of hand fitting operations that the Americans did not like, but the

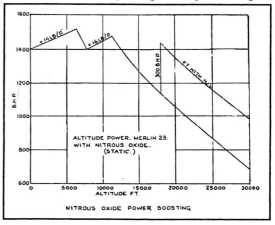

Fig.7: Power increase with Nitrous Oxide Injection.

problem with the epicyclic drive was the load on the planet gear bearings.

In the quest for more performance Rolls Royce concentrated on the development of Sir Stanley Hooker's two-stage supercharger (Fig.8) and, after the success of the Merlin 61 in the Spitfire Mk.IX, Mosquito MP469 was fitted with two Merlin 61's with modified cooling systems. In September 1942, this aircraft flying at a low weight reached 42,000ft and was still climbing at 500ft per minute!.

Cyril Lovesey, the Chief Development Engineer, favoured getting high power from more supercharge and 'doing it with petrol' rather than separate power-boosting systems with all their extra weight and time limitations on use. On the other hand the Merlin had shown itself capable of running for considerable periods at high boost pressures, the only time

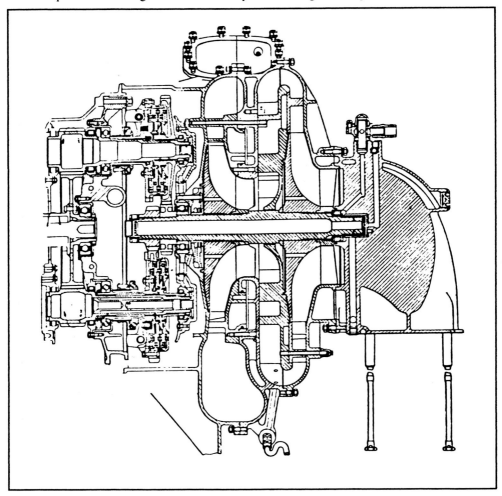

Fig.8: Sectional view through a two-stage supercharger, as fitted to the first high-altitude Mosquitoes.

Fig.9: The two-stage Merlin with S.U. Carburettor. The engine illustrated has a cabin supercharger drive taken from the reduction gear and in the Mosquito would be a Merlin 73. (Photo: Rolls Royce)

limitation being fuel capacity.

In consequence, high-altitude two-stage supercharged versions of the Merlin were used on the Mosquito in its PR, Fighter and Bomber roles.

The engine shown in Fig.9 is not in fact a 61 - it has a cabin blower mount and is very similar to the 73 as fitted to the Mosquito. It still has the SU carburettor, two stage blower and intercooler and the 'Universal' crank-case.

Fig.10: A Merlin 76/77 fitted with a Bendix carburettor (Photo: Rolls Royce)

21

First production models were 72 and 73. These had a first stage supercharger rotor diameter of 11 inches and 10.1 inches for the second stage. Supercharger gear ratios were 6.39 and 8.03:1. Maximum power on 100 octane fuel was 1,400hp at around 21,000ft and over 1,000hp at 30,000ft. When 150 octane fuel became available 21lbs of boost gave 1590hp at 17,500ft. These engines were succeeded by the Merlin 76/77, retaining the same supercharger gear ratios, but with the first stage impeller diameter increased to 11.5 inches and with the true circular arc rotating guide vanes.

This was virtually the same engine as the Merlin 66 for the Spitfire IX LF apart from the supercharger gear ratios but with the reversed flow cooling system. Instead of an Anti-G SU carburettor, a Bendix low pressure injection unit was fitted (Fig.10) with low pressure injection into the rotating guide vanes. The carburettor actually injected the fuel at five pounds per square inch as opposed to sucking it through jets below the throttle valves - a highly complex piece of equipment that, generally speaking, worked pretty well.

With the bigger first stage impeller maximum power using 100 octane fuel and FS Gear was 1,440hp at over 23,000ft. On 150 grade, the engine was cleared to 25lb boost, giving 1,950hp in MS Gear at 5,000ft and in FS 1750hp at 18,000ft. So the engine was just short of touching 2,000hp in MS Gear. With the lower-geared Merlin 66, 2,050hp at 25lbs boost was available, which was really doubling the horsepower from the Battle of Britain Merlin III.

In discussing night-fighter operations with Group Captain John Cunningham, he commented on the way which the Merlin would hold 23-24lb boost at 3,000rpm for as long as one wished to use it, with the engines showing no signs of distress.

The final version of the Merlin to be used in the Mosquito was the 113/114. The 100 series as the type was known was a major re-design, putting together hard-won combat experience at high powers. It was a sort of mid-war, mid-term re-design, thinking that things were going to go on for a long time. The crank-case was re-designed with strengthening features at the major stud locations, whilst an end-to-end lubrication system was adopted for the crankshaft.

As can be seen from the shaded area in Fig. 11 - the main pressure oil feed, there is a feed through the spring drive and a transfer tube going through the reduction gear pinion. There are no feeds through the crank-case to the main bearings. The feed is entirely end-to-end with de-aerating holes in the pins and journal caps. There are no lubrication grooves in the main bearings but there are standpipes in the end main bearings to get rid of the grit and foreign matter that was always present in oil. No one would ever consider the concept of a pressure filter during the war, and this acted as a very good 'muck separator' and engines of this nature were very good indeed. It is something that the motor car industry has singularly failed to adopt, but Tony Rudd, who worked for me on a service failure investigation on the Merlins and is now a Director of Lotus has embodied this on the latest Lotus and also the latest American Corvette which they developed for General Motors, and it works extremely well!.

The 100 series supercharger was a major departure from previous practice. While it retained the gear ratios and rotor diameters of the 76/77 the rotor arrangement was different. The traditional plain tail bearing, with its concentric floating bushes was deleted in favour of an inter-stage roller bearing, thus giving a better supercharger intake. Also embodied was

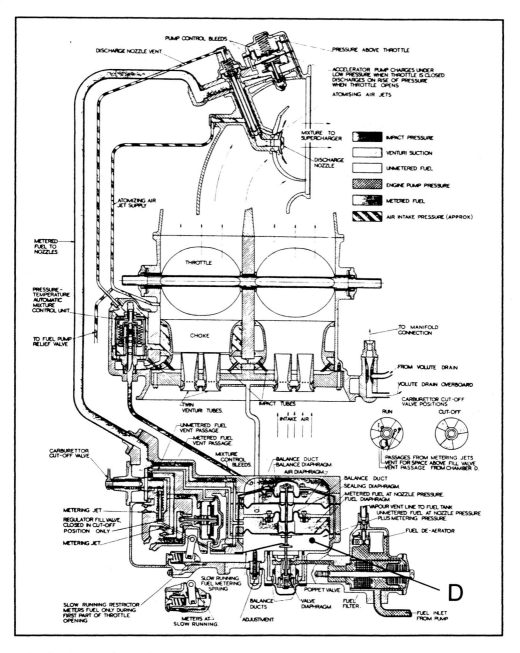

Fig.11: Diagram of a Bendix Carburettor. At the top is shown the 'spider' injecting fuel into the eye of the supercharger at 5lb per sq.in.

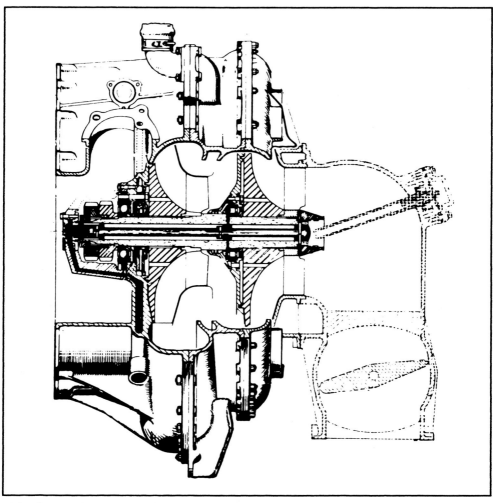

Fig.12: A section through a Merlin 100 series supercharger, showing overhung first stage impellor and fuel injection nozzle located to give best fuel atomisation

single point SU injection and single plate throttle with no venturis. The fuel injection was by the single pipe you see in Fig. 12, squirting into a cup formed in the retaining nut on the impeller shaft to give extremely good vaporisation of the fuel. It must be realised that the latent heat of evaporation of the fuel is worth 25°C reduction in the charge temperature and we were also taking around 100°C out of the charge by means of intercooling.

The Mosquito fitted with the Merlin 113/114 (Fig.13) only saw service operationally as a PR aircraft and was not used in bombers or fighters prior to VE Day and was therefore limited to 18 pounds boost. Some idea as to its potential can be gained from the fact that it gave 1000hp at over 35,000ft and was still giving 800hp at 40,000ft. There is no doubt that 25lbs boost

Fig.13: The Merlin 113/114 which saw service towards the end of the European war in the high-altitude PR Mosquito

would have been available for bomber and fighter types and 30lbs boost was on flight test at Derby in 1945.

Although not intended for the Mosquito, perhaps I could mention the 130 series Merlin (Fig.14) installed in the Hornet - this was the ultimate military Merlin. It differed in having a side-mounted coolant pump, and a down-draught induction to reduce frontal area. This was an engine that had to be poured into its powerplant like Jane Russell had to be

Fig.14: The ultimate military Merlin - the 130 series for the de Havilland Hornet, with design features to reduce frontal area. (Photo:Rolls Royce)

poured into her dresses!. It was a particularly neat engine, designed especially for de Havillands. Certain marks of this series featured a Corliss throttle to reduce throttle torque in the pilots hands and give a still cleaner intake with no throttle butterfly. Engines were paired, one having a conventional reduction gear, the other an idler gear fitted to provide handed rotation to improve aircraft handling.

The aero-engine has not been built that does not give trouble and continued effort is required to eradicate problems. Our basic rule in failure investigation was (and I still hope is in the company) 'there is no such thing as an isolated failure. The isolated failure of to-day is the epidemic of tomorrow'. By the time to Mosquito flew, the pressures of 1940 were showing in modified engines, with improved lubrication and other features. Also it was not long before the two-piece cylinder block - with its better joint integrity, and the ability to run at higher boost pressures - was on production engines.

Nevertheless, the unexpected will always arise, and it came in the form of reduction gear problems. Reduction gear bearing tracks were not flanged and were retained in thin steel housings by a light interference fit. After the aircraft had been in service for some time, the bearings outer races showed a tendency to spin. In the case of the rear propeller shaft bearing, not only did the race spin, but some apparent skewing of the rollers drove the race forward, wearing its retaining tabs and finally pushing it out of its housing, so that the propeller shaft was dependant on the front roller bearing and ball thrust bearing - thus the alignment of the shaft was not controlled. Investigations showed that with these close-set powerplants there was a passing frequency set up between the propeller blade tips and the fuselage at low rpm's. This was sufficient to cause the troubles mentioned. Above about 2,400 rpm the vibration reduced but, with the need to fly at lower rpm - down to 1,800 at up to 7lbs boost to give range, engines were frequently operating at severe vibration levels.

The answer was to harden the bearing locations and to fit a continuous retaining ring for the rear propeller shaft bearing, which was the worst affected. At the same time the energy in the vibration would set the bearing housing moving in its casting so again it was the rear propeller shaft bearing that suffered. The problem with the bearing housings were tackled by increasing the interference fit and compensate the bore size so that when fitted it did not put excessive interference on the race.

We hardened the housing bores by use of chromium plate, which had the advantage that its tendency to fret restrained the bearing movement. We also plated the front roller bearing location on the propeller shaft as well as the bores of the other reduction gear bearings.

Most of these modifications were embodied at overhaul, but the rear propeller shaft bearing problem required us to fit high interference housings with hardened bores, together with the continuous retaining ring as a field modification, which we successfully did using liquid oxygen.

If I may divert for a moment, there is a rather nice story about that. I set off one early one morning in the early summer of 1944 with a colleague in a Bentley with a open-necked, five-gallon flask of liquid oxygen sizzling quietly to itself on the back seat. We were pottering along at about 35 mph when John Nutter turned to me and suddenly said in one of those 'stiff upper lip' British wartime film voices 'I've just seen a Fw190'. I said 'It can't be - it must be a T-Bolt from one of the American squadrons'. He replied "I know an Fw190, look!'.

Sure enough, banking across in front of us was a Fw190. There had been rumours of long range 'Lone Ranger' flights attacking the supply columns just before the invasion in June 1944 and he said 'what are you going to do?'. I said 'well, you keep an eye on him, and when he comes round behind us we'll get out of the car and into the ditch'. John said 'He's turning, he's coming round' I said 'Alright, get ready to get out...' He then said 'Oh, he's put his gear down!'. Then of course we realised we were close to RAF Wittering home of the Hostile Flight. It was one of their aircraft going in to land!. Much orificial twitching took place!.

Looking back over the war years, it can only be said that the various marks of Mosquito, with their particular Merlin types, produced outstanding aeroplanes in all manner of roles and at all altitudes. In this connection one must not forget the Mosquito VI's and their success in the V1 season. Single stage Merlin 25's on 150 grade fuel provided the extra urge to deal with that nasty weapon.

If one considers the array of twin engined aeroplanes that flew with or fought against the Mosquito, one is not surprised at the envy with which the Mosquito and its Merlins were regarded by Allies and enemy alike".

Fig.15: Rolls Royce not only developed the engines. Here DD723, an NF.Mk.II is shown fitted with experimental Lancaster-type power units with underslung 'chin' radiators instead of the normal wing leading edge ones. This aircraft was tested at Rolls Royce Hucknall during the latter part of 1943 in an effort to solve the overheating and exhaust problems. (Photo: BAe)

Discussion

Charles Masefield took the Podium:

"Well, thank you very much Alec. I think you would all agree that Alec has talked about and described the Merlin with all the enthusiasm and clarity of someone talking about an engine that is still in production today. Thank you for that Alec - fascinating!.

You must be the only person that set off in a Bentley - many before with an open flask in the back , but the first that contained liquid oxygen!

I was reflecting that there really is nothing new in this world. The BAe146 engine - the Lycoming, which I am delighted to say is working beautifully now went through many years of reduction gear problems, being the first fan engine in the world to fly with a reduction gear. Exactly the same sort of solutions were finally integrated into that engine that you were talking about on the Merlin. I wonder why we are always so slow to learn the same lessons again. Now, could we have some questions or comments please?".

From the floor: "Good morning. I had the honour of flying Mosquito Night Fighters on 68 Squadron. I did have one trouble in that I had to bring one back on one engine. It was due to the sodium filling in the exhaust valve and was very impressed subsequently by the way in which Rolls Royce tackled the problem, even down to the British Steel works where the valves were made. I wonder if you would like to comment about that?. I did have two one-engined landings and the Mossie was beautiful to fly on one engine"

Alec Harvey-Bailey: "The Merlin exhaust valve had a sodium-cooled stem. I would think the problem was probably initiated by cracking of the valve tulip and a piece coming out of the tulip and the crack getting into the stem. This used to happen at around 360 hours of operation, but occasionally we did have a valve failure which was traced to non-rotation of the exhaust valves. Valve burning that would lead to loss of sodium was most unusual. On later engines we locked the bottom washer on the valve spring, fitted longer close-clearance valve guides to control the valve better and keep the valve rotating. On commercial engines cruising at about 800-850hp they would run up to 500 hours, but casualties of that nature were normally due to non-rotation. Of course occasionally with the thousands of valves that were produced it was possible to get a blow-hole in a weld that somebody missed. The valves had a Brightray coating over the underside of the tulip and on the seat, and the seat in the head was Stellited on most engines. I think that is really all I can say about that - we did recognise it as a problem".

The original questioner replied; "We converted from Beaufighters to Mosquitos and I had the pleasure of going to Derby for an engine handling course which was a great deal of help.

Alec Harvey-Bailey; "That was 68 Squadron you say?. Was that Wing Commander Mansfeld, the Czech?. Ah, I went up to I think Colby Grange when they were there, or was it Acklington for one week-end..."

From the floor: "The story of 68 Squadron was that it was founded by Max Aitken and it was half Czech, half English and Mirro Mansfeld, one of our distinguished Czechs was a Battle of Britain pilot and has been in the news all this year. Thank you sir".

From the floor: "How did it come about that Rolls Royce produced such a beautiful engine initially that could not cope with negative G in the early part of the war?. It seems quite remarkable that no-one ever thought about it...'

Alec Harvey-Bailey: "Well, it was known and it was thought about. It was said that the single-engined fighters would be tackling bomber formations and the negative 'G' manoeuvre would not be part of the combat regime. As a matter of fact we have here today a colleague of the late much lamented Tilley Shilling of the RAE who sorted it all out for us. She saw through a barn door much farther than most of us. She realised that the Merlin had a twin-geared fuel pump and this had been designed with a safety factor so that each would take the maximum requirement of the engine plus 20% with a relief valve in the system. When you got negative G the first thing that happened was that the engine went 'lean' because all the fuel rose in the float chamber, the float lost control and then there was this enormous 'squirt' of fuel from the two pumps, giving about twice the requirement of the engine. This caused it to fluff. Tilley introduced the RAE restrictor which limited the flow through the carburettor to something just over maximum take-off demand and that improved things a lot. She then introduced the 'Anti-G' version of the SU. Tilley did two things. She put a control on the setting of the float which limited the amount the needle valve came up when the float lost control, but also fitted an excrescance on the tip of the needle that acted like an RAE restrictor which cut off the flow under the negative G condition. There were also ball valves to stop the fuel flooding out of the carburettor through the air vents under negative G. This was all done retrospectively and it worked very well and is all due to the late Tilley Shilling , God bless her!"

Mr Darrant: " On the carburettor, at any time was water vapour added to the air intake?. We had some Merlins on some of the boats, and we had water vapour which went into the air intakes to increase performance"

Alec Harvey Bailey: "No. Water injection was tried, but we found that we could get all the power we wanted from boost pressure. Of course this would have meant another system - you add to the engine and Lovesey with his tremendous sleight of hand as a development engineer could always winkle another few pounds of boost pressure from somewhere.

It really didn't have a real application other than the one I talked about - that of Nitrous Oxide injection which was used on the Mosquito. Of course we had intercooling on two-stage engines. I talked about 40% of intercooling which is about 100° out of charge temperature on a two-stage engine. That is a compromise figure - in regard to the amount of charge cooling and the size of the intercooler radiator. And that just happened to be the practical compromise. No, we never used them on a production basis. We did use water injection on a very high power run at 36lbs boost and 2,640 hp endurance test, but that was really all it was used for".

Charles Masefield: "O.K., just one more please...".

Reg Davy: " I was a Mosquito Navigator - and as long as the two propellers went round, that was all we seemed to bother about!. Can you tell me how you measured horsepower? Was it done theoretically, or was it done with an instrument?"

Alec Harvey Bailey: "It was done on a dynamometer which measures engine speed and torque. You can get a very accurate reading - we had no way of reading in the aircraft. You read the power from the boost and RPM that you were getting, which was based upon test-bed figures and theoretical altitude corrections. We did try on the commercial engine to measure the deflection of the quill drive between the reduction gear and the crankshaft, but we never got power figures that the operators believed, so we threw it away!".

Charles Masefield returned to the podium:

"Well I have to call a halt there, but thank you very much Alec, for describing to us what undoubtedly was the great engine of World War Two and perhaps the engine that did as much as anything and indeed any aircraft to change the course of that conflict. The Merlin was the common theme that ran through all of those great aeroplanes - The Hurricane, Spitfire, Mosquito, Lancaster and the P-51. It was a quite remarkable engine and we all benefitted from the outcome of that conflict. Thank you, and all your team for what you did then, and thank you for your talk this morning".

CHAPTER THREE

A WOODEN WORK OF ART
Speaker - Mike Ramsden

The section started with Charles Masefield in the Chair:
"Now, finally in this morning's session before we break for a buffet lunch is Mike Ramsden. Mike is, of course today of the Royal Aeronautical Society - the main Society - and is the first of today's speakers from from the de Havilland Technical School. The first old boy and, I'm glad to say there are a number of those present to-day. Mike is a past Editor of 'Flight International' during, may I say, its golden period and of course the only true Roger Bacon. Mike, could you please tell us about the design and development of the first, the Mk. 1 aircraft?.

By the way, I very much hope that Mike will be interrupted during his talk by the sound of two Merlins as they taxi up to our window over there between the two hangars. The aircraft has been delayed from taking off from Chester due to weather, but I very much hope it is en-route by now".

Mike Ramsden took the Podium:
"Thank you very much Charles. This part is titled 'A Wooden work of Art' and I would like to begin by telling you of a coincidence. In the Royal Aeronautical Society we receive all kinds of technical papers and I just happened to spot one that came in last Friday. It was a NASA report about wood as an aircraft material of the future, written by two scientists who say, in effect, that wood has always been a great engineering material, the use of its strength only limited by joints. Now that we have Epoxy Resins and glues there is a great present and future for the material. In fact propeller blades of wood are being used in a NASA wind-tunnel, new power turbine windmills are using wooden blades and of course boats are going back to laminated wooden structures.

If I may just quote from this paper '*At a time when fibreglass was dominating the boat-building industry, a unique wood technology was developed that relied on a new plastic ingredient - Epoxy Resin. For the first time the industry possessed a key ingredient that could be used to both bond and seal wooden structures, permitting high strength-to-weight ratios that efficiently utilised wood's excellent physical properties. This upgrading of an old material with new technology has evolved considerably during the past two decades and is the basis for a revolution taking place in wood technology*'. So we are not talking about an aircraft of the past.

The prototype of the Mosquito - one of the most versatile combat aircraft ever built - flew just a month after the Hurricane and Spitfire won the Battle of Britain. In other words, 50 years ago today the official closing date of the Battle of Britain was only just over three weeks ago - and the Mosquito was about to fly (Fig.16).

The aircraft's structure was to bear more than 40 different burdens and was made of Nature's composite - wood. The Mosquito was described to me by Ralph Hare, who gave me

Fig.16: 50 years ago. The prototype Mosquito, with its earlier DH markings of E-0234, is prepared for flight under the cover of tarpaulins to prevent enemy observation from the air of its bright yellow shape. (Photo BAe)

a great deal of help with this paper and who was one of the original team at Salisbury Hall, as probably man's highest engineering achievement in timber.

In a letter to Sir Wilfrid Freeman, dated 20 September 1939, Sir Geoffrey de Havilland wrote "We believe we can produce a twin engined bomber which would have a performance so outstanding that little defensive equipment would be needed. This would employ the well tried out method of construction used in the Comet and the Albatross and being of wood or..." and he uses this word "...composite construction would not encroach on the labour and material used in expanding the RAF. It is especially suited to really high speeds because all surfaces are smooth, free from rivets, overlapped plates and undulations and it also lends itself to very rapid initial and subsequent production'." That was September 1939.

50 years after the Mosquitoes first flight, the wooden construction of this famous combat aircraft is still an object of wonder. If timber can be defined as 'nature's fibre reinforced resin' then the Mosquito was, in effect, the first high performance composite combat aircraft - light, strong and tough.

Of nearly 8,000 Mosquitoes carpentered in England, Australia and Canada from Spruce, Birch, Balsa, Ash, Douglas Fir and Walnut - those are all the different woods used in the aircraft - two or three are still airworthy, if you include the B35 in the Mosquito Aircraft Museum, which has recently been restored to what I think is better than original condition. It is in fact by any standards, an airworthy aircraft. All are free of the boring fatigue and corrosion troubles which afflict metal aircraft, although you do have to watch the water ingress problem - known for some reason as 'dry rot'. Wooden structures, like plastic composites, suffer from the glue-degrading effects of moisture and temperature, delamination and rot. But well looked after - not too damp, not too dry and kept in an even temperature - a wooden aeroplane should last as long as a piece of Chippendale.

One of my jobs as an apprentice here was installing Merlins and DH propellers on the production line. Although I did not have any experience of making the wooden structure, it was in doing this paper that I came to realise just what a marvel it is.

You can inspect the Mosquitoes structure at the DH Museum - it is a masterpiece of marquetry. A wing and an FB.6 fuselage are also being restored there by volunteers, so you can see just how it was made. When I was there, one of the wing restorers was working on the wing of the FB.VI which had been recovered from Israel where it had been out in the open for 20 years. He drew my eye to an amazingly small metal fitting which takes engine loads into the wing, and commented 'They knew what they were doing, didn't they?'. I think that could almost be the title of this paper.

At least two of the original team of nine designers are present with us to-day. Richard Clarkson and Ralph Hare are here, and I will be referring to Mr Clarkson's contribution in a moment. Ralph Hare, who gave me so much help in the preparation of this paper, was responsible for aircraft overall loads and for stressing of the wing. His distinguished structural career spanned the wings (and other aspects of the structure) of everything from Moths to the Airbus. The Mosquito was developed into more than 40 variants and the two Merlin engines we've heard so much about pushed it to 420mph at 30,000ft with a 4,000lb bomb-load. This structure carried the same bomb-load, I have been told, as a B-17 over the same range - Berlin and back from East Anglia at twice the speed and with one-sixth of the crew and perhaps 20% of the manufacturing man-hours. And although 'stealth' was not the 'in-word' then, the Mosquito probably had only 10% of the radar signature because of its wooden construction.

Fig.17: Bombing up DZ367, a B.Mk.IV of 105 Sqn.

The chief designer, R. E. Bishop, regarded the Mosquito as his greatest achievement. He never said so, but when I interviewed him about the Comet jet airliner in 1988, a year before he died, he was clearly most proud of the Mosquito. He asked me if I wanted to stay for lunch and, upon sitting down, he brought out some notes, which I expected to continue the interview about the Comet. In fact these were notes he had prepared about the Mosquito. He recalled how the standard British 500 lb. bomb was redesigned by his assistant, Tim Wilkins, so that four would fit into the Mosquitoes bomb bay instead of just two (Fig.17). Night after night, Mosquitoes with four 500 lb. bombs flew from England to Berlin and back - higher and faster than enemy fighters and, as we know, eventually carrying the 4,000lb bomb. The aircraft needed a crew of only two, and its structure made no demands on the hard pressed strategic resources of bauxite and metal machining. In fact it employed the skills and under-used capacity of the furniture industry. Mr Bishop recalled the words of Goering, who said: *"I turn yellow and green with envy when I see the Mosquito. The British knock together a beautiful wooden aircraft which every piano factory over there is making. They have the geniuses, I have the nincompoops".*

Another member of the original team, chief aerodynamicist Richard Clarkson, also helped me with this paper. He recalled: "We had estimated that the maximum speed of the Mosquito would be 376mph. When we measured it, it was 388mph - 23mph faster than the Spitfire. The Air Ministry said 'It cannot be faster than the Spitfire'." I think that may have been another title for this symposium really!

The official measurement at Boscombe Down, where the prototype W4050 was tested by Gp Capt. Allen Wheeler, confirmed the de Havilland estimate. After correcting the figures, Boscombe's Chief Technical Officer Fred Rowarth said to an anxious Clarkson: "I take my hat off to 387mph".

Ralph Hare remembers Bishop as leader of the small Salisbury Hall design team. "He was not a hierarchy man, and the hours he personally put in were staggering". Bishop had been responsible for the design of the Flamingo, de Havilland's first all-metal aircraft, but he had been brought up in the de Havilland tradition of wooden structures. Under A. E. Hagg - whom he had succeeded as chief designer in 1938 - the young Bishop saw how the DH88 Comet racer had innovated diagonal planking to achieve a thin wing of high aspect ratio without external bracing. This form of construction (faithfully restored in 1983-84 by RAE Farnborough's woodworking department for the surviving D.H.88 G-ACSS) had also been adopted for the very much bigger 1937 DH91 Albatross airliner for Imperial Airways. It was also looked at for the DH98 Mosquito, but it became obvious that this kind of construction was not going to take the loads.

Like most other members of the team, Bishop had practical hands-on experience in the factory as an apprentice. The result was not only a brilliant design, but one that could be, in the words of Goering, 'knocked together' by people who had perhaps never made aircraft before, including unskilled labour in furniture factories.

Ralph Hare recalls the daily journeys which he made during early 1940 in his 1933 Austin Seven saloon from Salisbury Hall, where the design work was going on, to Stag Lane, Edgware, carrying test pieces to the de Havilland materials laboratory there. The diagonal planking was of course tested, but was found wanting. He recalls that *"I must have taken hundreds of panels and specimens for strength testing before the final design decisions were made*".

The diagonal spruce wing planking would not take the loads required of the Mosquito. The bottom skin was not the problem; the top skin would not take the compression loads without buckling and failing. It was found that a double plywood sandwich, with span-wise stringers - first of spruce, later of Douglas Fir - was by far the most effective structure. The size of the square section stringers was calculated by theory, varying with wing station and checked by testing. The top of the single-piece wing comprises three double-skin panels.

Many panels were made for 'control tests', to measure the basic performance properties of the materials and the construction, to put numbers to allowable stresses in tension, compression and shear, and to measure elastic moduli, mean values being used to obtain stress distributions for design. Optimising these properties for the wing - the most heavily loaded part of the structure - was the ultimate test of de Havilland's timber experience. Two spars with tip-to-tip top and bottom booms of laminated spruce, boxed with plywood webs, were finally chosen (Fig.18).

Spruce has always been the standard wooden aircraft material. The tree grows very tall with very few knots, and it is blessed with the straight grain and low density which gives it the highest strength to weight ratio. Even so, only one in ten Canadian spruce trees was selected for construction of the Mosquitoes 50 foot spars. The choice of wood to meet the required

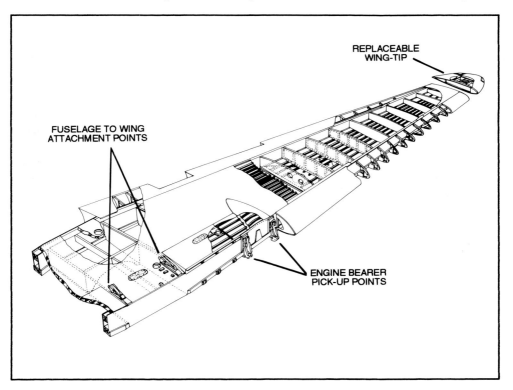

Fig.18: Details of the internal wing structure.

35

aircraft standards became a great skill. Air Ministry specification DTD 36B set out the requirements for aircraft spruce, defining moisture, density, brittleness, straightness of grain and other properties, how to test for them, and what the strengths and moduli should be.

The forward booms were made of single-piece spruce laminations; the aft booms - accommodating the famous Mosquito wing planform - had to have forward sweep as well as dihedral, and were spliced. Theory and experience, backed by the Stag Lane testing and what was required by DTD 36B, showed that 1 in 15 was the best taper for these splices. For hardwoods 1 in 10 was best.

The front spar booms were originally made of three horizontal laminations, and the aft spar of three vertical laminations to accommodate the forward sweep. In theory the booms could have been solid spruce beams, but laminations allowed easier manufacture and were the best use of spruce resources. In the course of production the three laminations became ten to save more wood. Sawing was accurate to within 0.01 in., left rough for the gluing.

The laminations and spar webs were glued in their jigs under pressure and, to speed up glue setting, were heated. Electric mats kept the temperature of the whole production jig constant regardless of whether one end of the fifty foot spar was near a draughty factory door or the other near a warm canteen. The accuracy of the spar over a length of 50ft. was 0.04 in - remarkable precision of 1 in 15,000 - not bad for mass production carpentry!

The gluing operation was as critical as it is with composites today. The laminated booms had to be at least as strong as single-piece booms. In fact, a well glued laminated spar could be stronger than a solid spar. Laminations also obviated the shrinkage and warping which single beams might suffer. The glue was at first casein, a milk-based adhesive with which de Havilland and other wooden aircraft manufacturers had had long experience, but which proved unsatisfactory because of fungal growth - when a damaged Mosquito tailplane was removed and the inside found to be full of mushrooms, the search for a new glue began. Casein was replaced by synthetic 'Beetle', made by Dr. N. A. de Bruyne's Aero Research company at Duxford (now Ciba-Geigy, which still makes the offspring adhesive Redux, used for BAe 146 wings and other metal structures today).

Testing and service experience showed that the wood fibres tore before the Beetle glue did. Tests of Mosquito spars - spruce booms boxed by plywood webs joined with glue and screws - showed that the booms nearly always failed before the glue.

Beetle, introduced in Britain in about 1942, was also more resistant to humidity and to the temperature cycling of Mosquitoes operated to high altitudes in all climates from the tropics of Asia to the arctic winter airfields of north Europe. Mosquitoes glued with casein would have deteriorated sooner, and probably none would have survived in airworthy condition to this day. But even Beetle has its weathering limits - as do the epoxy resins of today's composites. Redux, later used for gluing metal to wood veneer in the Mosquitoes successor, the DH103 Hornet fighter, is better even than Beetle, though it is essentially a hot-cured metal to metal adhesive.

There was a saying in the old de Havilland days, possibly attributable to DH himself: "You never glue without a screw". There were more than 30,000 brass screws in a Mossie's wing, and I know not how many more in the fuselage and tail. If we say 50,000 screws per Mosquito and my arithmetic is right, then that's 400 million brass screws in 8,000 Mosquitoes - so the aircraft did require some metal!. (Not forgetting of course the steel undercarriage, Merlins, DH propellers, engine and undercarriages mountings, elevators, canopy, wiring and plumbing).

Birch plywood found to give the best results was made of three plies laid at 45° to each other, so that when a shear load was applied, it was redistributed into a tension load along one ply grain and a compression load along the other two, the whole web taking a bigger load under compression.

The lower wing skin was to be a single plywood panel stiffened with spruce stringers. The lower spar booms were reinforced round the tank door cut-outs with strips of ash (originally compressed birch) to deal with the high concentration of tank door bolt loads. The bolt bearing edges of the tank doors were similarly reinforced with the hard plastic impregnated laminated fabric called 'Tufnol' - an ancestor of today's structural plastics.

Ash reinforcings extended along the bottoms of each spar boom to the outboard tank rib - about two thirds of the the span. Compared with compressed birch, ash was found on test to have a better sensitivity to holes and other notches.

The wing ribs were conventional; Rib One had a top boom of five spruce laminations, with a bottom boom of Douglas Fir and a three ply web. Ribs Three and Four took metal fittings for the engines and undercarriage.

The Mosquitoes fuselage, made in halves by stretching two skins of birch plywood over concrete moulds remains unique in aircraft construction. The plywood - three 1.5mm to

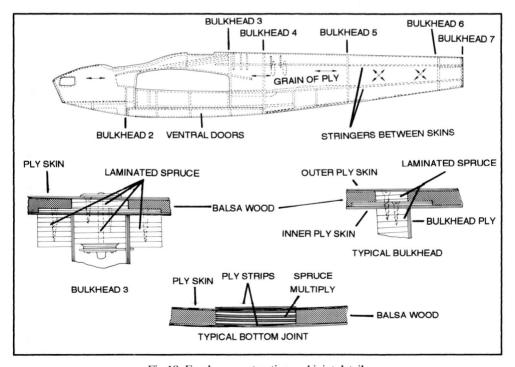

Fig.19: Fuselage construction and joint details

37

2mm, 45° diagonal plies - were stretched cold over the concrete mould, into which the bulkheads and other structural members had been slotted. Steel straps then stretched the plywood to its double curvature shape. Before the second skin was applied, 3/8 in thick balsa fillings were inserted to stabilise the structural sandwich (Fig.19).

Balsa, the very light softwood favoured by aero-modellers, was inserted in small pieces. Even though it was a tropical product, and therefore a U boat target, balsa had been the first choice for filling material, as it had worked well in the Albatross. A static test Albatross fuselage had used an expanded artificial rubber called Onazote; but this had unsatisfactory properties, including the 'rotten eggs" smell of hydrogen sulphide. Tests showed that the allowable stress of a birch plywood panel went up from 1,500 lb. per sq in. to 5,000 lb. per sq.in with a balsa sandwich core. Balsa weighs only 8 lb. per cubic foot: spruce weighs 28 and birch 45 lb. per cubic foot.

The finished half fuselage shells were edged with male to female laminated spruce wedge joints, glued and screwed. Before the joining, each shell was fitted with its wiring, plumbing and equipment. Thus the production workers didn't get in each other's way. The Mosquitoes designers separated the installations for ease of production so that electrics were in one fuselage shell and hydraulics in the other. Of course the fuselage had to be made in halves anyway, because of the double curvature limitation of plywood: but this limitation was turned to manufacturing advantage. Internal equipment was screwed to plastic "ferrules" glued and tacked to the walls through templates.

The inside of the fuselage shells and wing panels were sprayed with green or white water-resisting paint, and external surfaces sprayed with red paint and covered with 'Madapolam' fabric before final undercoat and camouflage.

Walnut, a strong hardwood, was used where the steel fuselage-to-wing attachment bolt loads had to be distributed. The walnut carried bearing loads from the bolts. The loads thus picked up by the walnut were transmitted to the supporting structure by the glued joints. The steel wing attachment fittings, like those carrying the engines and undercarriage, were remarkably economical of material and therefore weight.

The tailplane and fin were miniature versions of the wing. The elevators were made of aluminium (the skin was changed from fabric to aluminium to cure an aero-elastic problem experienced by the prototype). The rudder and ailerons were made of metal, fabric covered.

The undercarriage, in order to save precision machining resources and leaks, was sprung with rubber blocks inside struts made of flange riveted steel pressings developed from the company's pre-war series of light aircraft and airliners. There is a story of a Mosquito which had a Halifax land on top of it and which did not collapse - as much of a tribute to the undercarriage as to wood. The rubber blocks in each strut made very good tin-bashing mallets as many ex-de Havilland apprentices still find!.

The Mosquito was astoundingly tough. The timber mass of the Mk. 18 absorbed the recoil of a 57 mm howitzer right under the pilot (Fig.20). The structure could also tolerate impact damage. Such are the shock absorbing qualities of timber, properties shared with the great warships of Nelson's day. Hare recalls that one Mosquito, short of fuel after a photo recce flight over Genoa, made an emergency landing at a temporary airfield near Cobham, writing off three Beaufighters. It was repaired and flying again in six weeks.

Fig.20: The prototype Mk.18 - HJ732/G (The 'G' suffix denotes that the aircraft was to be guarded at all times). The aircraft was rapidly converted from a FB.Mk.VI series 1 machine and the barrel of the Molins 6lb gun is clearly visible under the Browning .303" machine guns in the nose.
(Photo: BAe)

The Mosquito was easy to repair in the field - carpenters just chipped out the damage and spliced in new sections with glue and screws. Workshop data sheets based on de Havilland calculations and tests for use in the field specified the size and depth of screw holes to achieve the best strength for given grain widths and lengths.

Wood is not a plastic composite analogue, but both materials have uni-directional grain and need strengthening if they are to take multidirectional stresses - hence plywood is more useful than timber straight from a tree. Wood cannot always be grained to the stress, as composite prepregs can, but natural fibres have more in common with man-made filaments than with aluminium. Wood can even be better than composites for the lighter aircraft structures.

Whilst the worst enemy of wooden structures is damp, the 50 year old Mosquito prototype W4050 is in better condition than many metal aircraft of its age. Bishop and his team designed in resistance to the elements as well as strength, performance and ease of manufacture. The Mosquito proved that metal is not the only material for high performance aircraft. Tomorrow's combat aircraft will also be made of composites".

Discussion.
Charles Masefield again took the chair.
"Thank you very much Mike. Never has there been such a eulogy of wood as a material for building aircraft. Magnificent!. I must admit, I have never thought of the Mosquito as the worlds first composite combat aircraft, nor as the first stealth bomber and fighter, but

nevertheless it is. I'm pleased to say our own Mosquito will be landing in two or three minutes and will be there for everyone to inspect. I have absolutely no doubt that when the Hatfield RAeS meet in this building to celebrate the 100th anniversary of the Mosquito, the same aircraft will be taxiing in for inspection for those gathered. Can we please now have any questions or comments for Mike?"

Barry Thorpe. "You gave us a very lucid description of the wooden construction, diagonal planking, sandwich construction and so on. One imagines that this gave a very stable structure. How much problem was there in service with warping, and indeed rigging the aircraft in the first place?"

Mike Ramsden: "It's not a problem I have had any experience of - it's not something I have heard about in my researches or talking to people. I do not know whether there are better people with the experience here to-day...?".

Ed Martin: " I was a rigger on 23 Squadron. We certainly had a Mosquito that would not fly properly and no-one knew why. When I came to Hatfield as an apprentice, I went over to Leavesden one day, and there was that very same aircraft sitting in one corner with everyone trying to find out why".

From the audience came the comment: "Did you get a new pilot?"

From the floor: "With regards to the ply/balsa/ply composite structure, would it be the fact that the two tough, strong ply parts were separated at a distance by the balsa created strength rather than the inherent strength of the balsa? Just one other point, I think that balsa is technically a hard, not soft, wood".

Mike Ramsden: "The balsa is not in the wing. That top skin or panel of the wing is in fact a box of plywood skin top and bottom held stable by Douglas Fir stringers. The balsa goes into the fuselage, so there is a difference between the fuselage and the wing. The existence of space does not I think make any difference. The reason for both forms of construction was a box stabilised by either balsa or Douglas Fir stringers to take to torsional loads".

Frank Vann: "Perhaps I could answer both of those questions. When de Havillands first introduced plywood sheeting on wooden aeroplanes instead of crossed wires with turnbuckles, one of the big advantages claimed was that you did not get the warping you used to get when you had to go around twiddling all the turnbuckles to pull the fuselage straight. I think that experience showed that use of plywood panels prevented warping occurring. Certainly no-one has produced a hard case that demonstrated that warping did occur on a Mosquito, so I would assume that it didn't happen.

In the other case, if you have two thin sheets of plywood and you want to carry a bending moment, the further apart you can get them the more load you can carry effectively. The only problem is that thin ply buckles under compression, and the way to prevent this is by putting some sort of support in vertical to its surface. And that was the function of the balsa. It does not carry any load of its own. I hope that Ralph Hare will confirm this?"

Ralph Hare: "Yes. One of the problems with a structure consisting of thin sheet, which has to carry load either in compression or in shear, is that it will buckle under these loadings and so limit the amount it can carry. One of the 'arts' is to support the thin sheet against that buckling so that it can carry very much larger loads. The balsa does this as well as carrying some of the end loads. The direction of the grain of the balsa was along the fuselage and was thus able to carry some of that loading in that direction, but it was not put there primarilly for that purpose. It was there to support the skin against buckling, as the stringers on the wing skin do, and as the reinforcing members on the webs of the spars do.

You mentioned this question of directional loading. It is very important. We did have one case where the spar webs had been put on upside down, and they wanted us to accept it. The fact that the grain was running in the wrong direction meant that its strength was nearly halved.

Buckling is the enemy of structural loading. Supporting against this will increase that structural loading significantly.

I would like to go back to a previous question if I may - this question of an unarmed bomber. This goes back in Captain DH's experience in the First World War, where similarly the DH4 as a bomber was able to outstrip the fighters of the day, and show that that defensive type of armament - speed - was an acceptable principle. When the people went along to the Ministry, they of course had not connected that possibility and it was not their philosophy. All they thought was that there should be a gun turret somewhere which was capable of shooting down half the Luftwaffe in one go"

From the floor: "Good morning. Would you like to comment on the effectiveness of wooden aircraft as against the metal-skinned aircraft in respect of taking enemy aircraft fire?".

Mike Ramsden: " I think wooden structures are capable of taking an enormous amount of punishment and damage, as indeed metal aircraft are. This of course is apparent from many photographs of damaged Mosquitoes. I don't know if there is much to choose - perhaps there are better experts that I on this subject of battle-damage resistance', but the Mosquito was probably easier to repair than a metal aircraft".

John Maynard: " I saw with enormous interest in this splendid book a project drawing of a twin-Goblin Mosquito development. Appreciating that the Vampire and Venom preserved the wooden structure, at least as far as the fuselage is concerned, was there a structural design limitation that prevented a jet powered Mosquito going ahead, thereby providing an 'earlier Canberra' if I can put it that way. Or was it purely a political decision?"

Mike Ramsden: " I don't think that there is anything to limit the use of a jet engine from the airframe material point of view. After all, the Vampire, some of which are still flying today, has a wooden fuselage".

David Tipper: "I was struck by the large amount of structural research that seemed to be necessary for the Mosquito and the very small amount of time into which it had to be fitted. Can you offer any enlargement on this?"

Mike Ramsden: "Only to share your astonishment!. We heard earlier from Mike Bowyer that the visit to the Air Ministry by Sir Geoffrey and Charles Walker to promote this project took place in 'late November 1939' There was nothing other than outline drawings in existence at this time. Within one year the prototype was flying. I think it is astonishing".

Charles Masefield took the chair.

"Well ladies and Gentlemen, all things Mosquito must run to programme of course, and we now are exactly on programme for completing this session. Thank you Mike for that paper. There is absolutely no doubt that when aircraft do return to wood as a standard method of construction, right here in this room to-day is the fount of knowledge of 'all things wooden'. We must make sure that everything that is said to-day is preserved for posterity and we know where to come to seek the answers in the future".

CHAPTER FOUR

RECOLLECTIONS OF AN APPRENTICE
Speaker - Frank Cooper

Tony Saint took the podium as Chairman and opened the first afternoon session.

"Good afternoon Ladies and Gentlemen. My name is Tony Saint and for your general interest I usually caretake the place around here, but for this afternoon I have the privilege of actually standing up here and chairing this session for this wonderful anniversary of the Mosquito event.

I must say that looking at the faces around, and certainly feeling the rapport of the various people in here, I know that you are getting a lot of enjoyment out of it and you've got more enjoyment to come and more memories from memory lane.

Firstly, Mr Frank Cooper, a de Havilland Apprentice, who will give you recollections of his time on the Mosquito, and certainly of his early days of doing an apprenticeship which I am sure that will have some similarities to today's apprentices, but also many differences I guess, not least of which will be the rate of pay, no doubt!.

That will be followed by Frank Vann, who I actually do know. Frank will be talking about production techniques. Frank comes from a wealth of experience of this site and certainly of the aeroplane. This will be followed by Pat Fillingham, who will be talking about test flying early Mosquitoes and then this session will conclude with Michael Bowyer, really looking again to how the marque evolved into the very many variants of the aeroplane that it actually got into. So, without more ado, can I turn you over to Frank Cooper. Thank you Frank".

Frank Cooper took the podium.

"Thank you. Well, first of all, I would like to say what a privilige it is to be asked to say a few words here this afternoon. I hope you are all sitting comfortably - but maybe not too comfortably, because my job is to try and keep you awake for the first twenty-five minutes or so after lunch!.

Now, 'Recollections of an apprentice...' It's a fine title to be given, because it is so broad-based that you can say what you like, and of course anything that you say is totally unaccountable!. I would like in fact, to try and give you an idea of what it was like to grow up young and impressionable through the thirties and the forties, starting from my earliest recollections of an obsession with aircraft engineering, and a determination that one way or another, I was going to be an aircraft engineer.

During the thirties, I was fortunate enough to live in this area and so I saw a lot of de Havillands, and I saw a lot of de Havilland aeroplanes. I was familiar with all the types, the Moth and the small airliners, the Comet Racer, and I was also able to spend a lot of time staying at Croydon near the then London airport,where I saw the big airliners of the day, such as that magnificent great biplane the Handley Page 42, which looked a bit like the Forth Bridge. I learned in later years, when I ran across the the son of the designer of the H.P.42 that it was designed a bit like the Forth Bridge too!.

Anyway, to get on. Come the war, the phoney war; Dunkirk; and the Battle of Britain. A Hurricane chasing a German bomber at roof-top height, right over my head, letting fly with his eight Brownings at just about the point where my ears were on the peak response of the shock waves. It was one hell of a noise, followed a few seconds later by dead silence broken only by the tinkle of the ammunition clips falling on the roof-tops and on the road. Bombs in the middle of the night, screaming down one after the other. I counted three screams and bangs, waited for the fourth which did not come. The German aeroplane throbbed away into the distance. The next day I went out and looked at the craters and trembled a bit when I saw that the fourth one would just about have been on me.

Anyway, to return to my theme. I did eventually join the firm as an apprentice aircraft mechanic fitter. I went to Salisbury Hall and started work there. The de Havilland Aeronautical Technical School had some twelve months previously succeeded the Mosquito team as occupants of the old house. It is also interesting to note that the first Airspeed Horsa Glider was built at Salisbury Hall, in the hangar taken over as the apprentice workshop.

So went my time at Salisbury Hall. I'd like to say at this point, what a great educational experience the old DH Tech School was. Not only was it good from an engineering training point of view, but also certainly left in me, a great feeling of team-work and dedication to aircraft and the industry, which I have never lost.

Salisbury Hall (Fig.21) was full of stories from its long history. There was a little building by the moat that was known as Nell Gwyne's Cottage and the story went that she, during one of the visits to the Hall by King Charles II held a baby out of the window over the

Fig.21: The entrance to Salisbury Hall - note the sentry-box and sandbags!. (Photo: BAe)

water and screamed at the King 'Recognise your son or I'll drop him". Whereupon the King is supposed to have replied "Don't drown the Duke of St Albans!"

I suppose the most interesting story that was all the rage when I was at Salisbury Hall was about the time when Geoffrey de Havilland and Fred Plumb persuaded one of the local farmers to breech a fence so that they could take-off W4052. This avoided the tedium of dismantling the aircraft for the short road journey to Hatfield, but as it was only the second Mosquito ever built it must have been a pretty risky business.

During my later days at Salisbury Hall (Fig 22), a Comet Racer - G-ACSS, the one that is now flying again and I am sure you are all familiar with, turned up at Salisbury Hall on a truck. It was then blue and silver; it had lost its red paint and 'Grosvener House' name from the Australian air race days. It was called 'The Burberry' and had the Burberrys coat of arms on the side of the fuselage. Apparently it had been parked in the open on the edge of Gravesend aerodrome since the beginning of the war. As you may remember, Gravesend was a fighter station during The Battle Of Britain, and I don't suppose anybody could be bothered with looking after an old Comet Racer, so it was in a very sad state indeed. The plywood was peeling where the damp had got in and it was just falling to bits - a sad business that but at least it was now safely stored. At about this time I finished at Salisbury Hall and moved on to Hatfield.

Hatfield was then a real bustle of a place, it was all go, go, go! Mosquito production

Fig.22: The later days of Salisbury Hall, with further hangars and buildings to give additional manufacturing and assembly facilities. (Photo: BAe)

45

was building up to full bore, and it really was an experience to remember.

This whole area of Hertfordshire was much more rural in those days, so getting to work at Hatfield posed a bit of a problem. Many of the roads that are now opened up and in fair shape were then just winding country lanes. There was very limited public transport at that time of the War - most of us therefore had to fend for ourselves. My particular contribution to road hazards at the time was a 1934, ten-horse power saloon. It was quite nippy, but unfortunately the chassis design did not take care of the power of the engine very well.

I was going to work one morning - late of course as usual - round a blind corner. I realized that the road in front of me was blocked, so I floored the brake pedal; but this produced only a gentle effect. I thought of the well known advice: "forget your brakes and steer". So that is what I did. I had the choice of three collisions, one was another small saloon, (I think it was a Ford-8) the second was a large Army truck filled with Italian Prisoners-of-War and the third was a cow - I chose the Ford-8 and hit him with a heck of a bang on his back bumper. The reactions were actually quite interesting: the driver of the Ford-8 got out looking thoroughly shocked; the Italian prisoners waved their hats in the air cheered and shouted something in Italian, which perhaps fortunately I did not understand; and the cow looked at me accusingly, mooed and walked gently off into the field!   Anyway, to get back to the point again.

My first job at Hatfield, which was really the job that brought me into contact with the Mosquito in a big way, was in the Inspection Department. We were accommodated in what was known in those days as the old pilots hut. This was a pre-fabricated building, right out on the airfield end of the main erecting shop. It accommodated not only our little section, but also some offices which were occupied by Rolls Royce Engines Representatives and an office which housed some people from the Air Ministry Inspectorate - it also accommodated the Works Barber.

The 'Works Barber' was a very useful organization because it meant just a quick phone call got you an appointment, then you'd get your hair cut. It was said that the whole logic of the provision of the barbers shop was that as your hair grew in the company's time, you could justifiably get it cut in the Company's time. I am not sure of this logic, but it was certainly a useful facility.

The Barber sold all the sorts of things that Barbers always sold in those days - and he had one interesting notice on his wall. I suppose society wasn't then quite as sexually enlightened as it is today. In deference to the young ladies who worked in the adjacent offices there was a big notice on the wall of the barbers and it said," Ask for the usuals or just give 2/6". I'll leave that one with you...

The main function of our section in the department was trouble shooting problems on the production lines (Fig.23). We had a little additional workshop which was a partitioned-off area on the bomber line that was manned twenty four hours a day so that we could always give an on-call service. We worked on aeroplanes during production on the line; for instance, when a hydraulic system failed on its production test. At these times solutions were required with the utmost urgency and we worked closely with the hydraulic test department and with others who were concerned with the systems on the Mosquito. Excellent experience for me as a young apprentice.

Fig.23: Ready for assembly!. 24 Mosquito mainplanes, complete with flaps and wearing full RAF camouflage and roundels await transportation to the final assembly shop. (Photo: BAe)

One memory that does remain with me very very strongly indeed was the attitude among the workforce on the Mosquito production line at Hatfield in those days (Fig.24). We were of course living through a period where history was being made. The activity that was going on, on the battlefields, on the oceans and in the air, we felt we were involved with because we were there to provide the Royal Air Force with one of the finest aeroplanes that they have ever possessed - it was up to us to keep these aircraft rolling out. The sense of dedication and sense of direction had to be experienced to be fully understood.

Of course the working conditions were a bit unique - we had the black-out morning and night. We came to work in the dark most of the year, we went home in the dark. But we were provided twice a day with 'music while you work' - the BBC put this out for half-an-hour in the morning and half-an-hour in the afternoon which was relayed all round the factory. We ate whale meat steaks in the canteen and goodness knows what else, but it was a fine experience.

One thing about this job that I found a bit disappointing initially was that there did not seem to be any opportunity for scrounging flights. However, it did have the advantage of providing a grandstand view of all the flying that went on, and once again I have to say, and I know there are one or two of the pilots here, I say it in all sincerity - the flying then, had to be

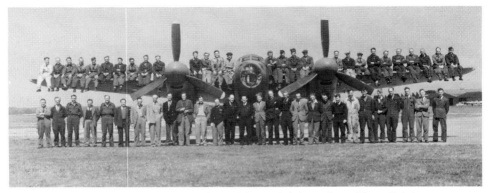

Fig.24: Some of the Mosquito builders and their product. (Photo: BAe)

seen to be believed. You don't see flying like that these days.

They used to come down very often over the St. Albans Road at almost zero feet and full bore across the airfield, just clear of the factory, then pull-up over Manor Road in a rolling climb - one engine sometimes stopped and feathered.

One particular instance I remember vividly still, because I thought we were going to have a catastrophe at the time, involved the de Havilland 100, a jet design that eventually became the Vampire. I don't know what I was doing, (probably wasting time) out on the edge of the airfield, watching the aeroplanes. The jet was pointing out across the airfield in front of the Experimental Department and there was a Mosquito coming in over Manor Road, with his exhaust crackling away as they did at closed throttle.

I was watching the landing and then I saw the jet start to take-off. Just at the wrong moment, the jet pilot opened up and he accelerated forward and I realized that he hadn't seen the Mosquito. The two aircraft were running on a collision course, with the DH100 about 90 degrees to the side of the Mosquito track. The Mosquito pilot saw him and opened his taps. The D.H.100 performed the most incredible take-off I have ever seen. He whipped the wheels up (fortunately, the DH100 had a very fast undercarriage retraction). The aircraft rose off the ground in a climbing turn with the port wing tip and the port tail boom both hitting the ground, raising the dust. As he went over the Mosquito, the slipstream from the latter lifted him away.

This morning we were told about the construction of the Mosquito and talked about the wings but it reminded me of a job that I had to do on a wing. I got involved with the wing for reasons I never really understood, except that there was some doubt about the wing glue joint strengths on a particular sub-contractors production. So, we were given one which had come off a service aeroplane. It was dumped in front of the old pilots hut and another apprentice and myself, were presented each with a hand-saw and told to cut the wing down all the screw lines. We flogged away at this for quite some time, cutting the wing with a hand-saw. We tried as far as we could to cut all the screws in half - the brass screws that you've heard about: however many hundreds of them there were in a wing.

What we got was interesting, it was in fact a Beetle-glued wing and the screws had all been put in with a hammer because you could see where the fibres went back from the screw tips. The tests that we did on the glue joints were all 100%: in every case the glue was stronger than the wood. So whatever the suspicion was, we didn't confirm it.

Another thing that we used to do from time to time which left impressions on us young fellows was to go into the Mosquito Repair Organization. We used to stand there looking at these aeroplanes that had come back by road from the Bomber Squadrons, damaged in all sorts of ways; shot to bits, some of them.

I think it is incredible that an aeroplane can be treated like that and still get its crew back (Fig.25).

Well, I have now a lot of memories of manufacture. The Mosquito was in fact carried right through the production line process on a couple of trolleys - one under each wing. There were two lines, one for Fighter variants and one for Bomber and Photographic Reconnaissance variants. At the beginning of each line the wing was put on the trolley and the fuselage lowered to enable the wing-to-fuselage joints to be made. From there the aircraft moved sideways down one side of the shop, across the back and along the other side, gathering canopies, engines, undercarriages and all the other parts that together made a complete aircraft. At the end of the line each aircraft was stood on its own wheel for the first time and the propellers fitted. It was then pushed into the paint shop next door. Fairly well up the line, pits had been dug to accomodate the wheels so the undercarriage retraction work could be done.

During my time at Hatfield, - 1943-44 - it was the peak of production and I think I am right in saying that in two years Hatfield produced just over 2000 aeroplanes. Which was quite something.

Fig.25: How they came back - A FB.Mk.VI belonging to 248 Sqn of the Banff Strike Wing. The aircraft struck the mast of the ship it was attacking in the Kattegat on 4 May 1945.

Fig.26: A number of Mosquitoes were sold abroad after the war. Here is '542' a T.Mk.III about to be delivered to the Turkish Air Force. (Photo BAe)

As D-Day approached, we knew something was up because our airfield was covered with new aeroplanes. The production was built up so that aeroplanes were there, ready for quick delivery into the service. I've seen 120 Mosquitos complete standing on the field like that. They were painted with recognition stripes, the black- and-white stripes for the D-Day landing. And then came D-Day itself.

Hatfield was under the run of the paratroop aircraft to France for D-Day itself, and it was an incredible sight. The sky was absolutely black with aeroplanes - Dakotas, Stirlings, Halifaxes - some towing gliders, some full of troops themselves. We watched this and thought this must be the beginning of the end. It seemed incredible to see so many aeroplanes flying out to assault the French coast on D-Day.

Soon after, it was time for me to move departments, and I came to the end of my association with the Mosquito. I went on around the factory. After the War I finished up at Panshangar, which was another nice place to work - like all the de Havilland Organizations, first class.

The Mosquito still had one trick to show me that I had never seen before. I happened to be at Hatfield after the War on a day when there was a demonstration. We were trying hard, I think, to sell surplus Mosquitos to various foreign Governments (Fig.26). There was a Mosquito up doing his fairly standard demonstration runs down over the St Albans Road, across the field, up over Manor Road - rolling and so on. He did it at full bore, then with one engine stopped and feathered. There was silence and we thought he'd gone home. Then it re-appeared, coming over flight test, where we were standing, it was almost down on the deck, going like mad with both stopped and feathered! It went across the field pulling up over Manor Road - start 1 - start 2 - and away those Merlins went! We thought 'that's a demonstration of confidence in reliability if anything is'.

That really brings me to the end of what I was going to say except, well, you might ask, 'what happened to me?' I eventually ended up at de Havilland Propellers, stayed there for 40 years, and retired last year. I have had a very satisfying career in this industry and it all started from the old DHAeTS. And from the first aeroplane I ever worked on, that remarkable Mosquito".

Tony Saint returned to the podium:
"Well, all I can say is well done Frank. That was a wonderful recollection of a lifetime there really. Unfortunately, although it all went so quickly, it also used up some of the time for the next speaker, so there is no time for questions. Anyway, thank you very much for that Frank".

CHAPTER FIVE

PRODUCTION
Speaker - Frank Vann

Mr Tony Saint at the podium:
"I would now like to introduce Mr Frank Vann, a production and design engineer extraordinaire who will now give you his views on some of the production techniques of that era".

Mr Frank Vann took the podium.
"I find myself in rather a unique position this afternoon, for I think I am the only speaker who hasn't had practical experience of working on the Mosquito. I am surprised to see that so many people who designed the Mosquito have survived, but I haven't managed to contact many people who produced the Mosquito, so maybe that says something about the rigours of the two jobs - I don't know.

In view of the fact that almost 8000 Mosquitos were built at locations scattered over three continents, it is obviously not possible in thirty minutes or so to give a comprehensive review of the whole story of Mosquito production. There is only time to review the most salient points and to give a brief description of some of the production techniques employed.

What I would like to do is first talk about some of those production techniques - those that haven't already been exposed to you by previous speakers, which I will pass over quickly. Then, I would like to talk about the history of where the production of the Mosquito took place, and the problems that were associated with the great orders that came in so quickly once the aeroplane was accepted.

I think the first thing to remember of course is that the Mosquito, as far as de Havilland's were concerned, wasn't a new concept, for they already had experience in building a high speed wooden aircraft with the Comet Racer. In fact, de Havilland's were one of the great proponents of wooden aircraft, when everybody else was changing over to metal.

But some of the techniques used on previous aeroplanes, did find their way into the Mosquito, in particular the balsa sandwich which came from the DH 91 Albatross, and the stringer-stiffened wooden wing which came from the Comet Racer.

A lot of thought was given to the design of the Mosquito for production needs. As soon as the Ministry had made it clear that large-scale production would be required, de Havilland's were able to invest in more sophisticated tooling and to plan production on a very efficient basis. Of course in those days cost wasn't the main importance; the main consideration was to get aeroplanes out to the RAF.

I think one of the big innovations was this idea of splitting the fuselage down the centre-line. Each half consisted of a sandwich shell, formed from an inner and outer spruce plywood skin separated by a core of balsa wood and also some wooden formers (Fig.27).

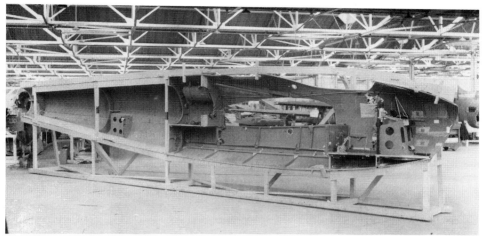

Fig.27: A good example of how the Mosquito fuselage was built in two halves, split vertically. As can be seen, some internal equipment has already been installed. (Photo:BAe)

Because the two halves of the fuselage were manufactured separately, the installation of much of the additional internal equipment and services could be made before the two halves were joined together.

Each half of the fuselage was initially built in the horizontal position with the joint face downwards. Male formers were constructed representing the inside shape of the fuselage shell; originally these were made of mahogany, but I think it was Harry Povey who proposed that concrete would be an easier material to get hold of and it would be cheaper too; so all the later aeroplanes were built on cast concrete formers.

There were internal formers as there are in any aeroplane and to accommodate these, slots had to be cut into these moulds - cut into the mahogany or cast into the concrete - to accommodate these formers inside and other bits of equipment.

So, first of all, these internal members were laid into the slots in the mould, and then, what would become the inner skin of the fuselage - which was three-ply birch wood, was then placed over these glued structural members. The rear fuselage was really single curvature, so there wasn't any difficulty in doing that - the skin was simply wrapped around the mould. In areas of sharp curvature - like the front fuselage, you could not form the ply wood into the three-dimensional shape very easily, and in those cases, narrower strips of ply were laminated together using scarfed glued joints to give the required double curvature shape.

Having got all that in position, steel straps were placed over the assembly. The straps were tightened with turnbuckles, which held the whole thing together until the glue had cured. There were holes provided in the straps to allow the excess glue to escape.

When the glue had set, the straps were removed for the next stage in the assembly. Between the inner and outer skins was a stiffening structure of spruce members. They were laid in place on top of the inner skin, as were the reinforcing strips that went round doors and cut-out apertures. The spaces left between the spruce members were filled with balsa wood blocks, cut individually to fit one at a time, removed and glued, then replaced. The steel bands were re-fitted and tightened over the assembly again while the glue set.

When all that had set, the steel bands were then removed again and the outer surface was smoothed off to form an absolutely uniform surface. The outer birch ply was then put on top of that with glue. The steel bands were yet again put back and tightened up. When that was all finished and had set, you had a half fuselage. One of the descriptions that we used was 'like a lobster shell'.

The completed fuselage halves were now taken off the moulds and mounted vertically in special fixtures. For speed and ease of production as much as 60% of the internal fittings were later bolted to the fuselage side by means of ferrules embedded in the fuselage structure before joining the halves together. As much of the equipment to be installed was pre-drilled, these ferrules had to be accurately located to match up with the existing holes in the equipment. Accurate templates were used to drill a number of holes into the internal skin of the fuselage and part way into the balsa core. In these holes were glued the ferrules consisting of a plywood disc carrying a wooden plug in which was located a threaded metal ferrule - to pick up the bolts attaching the equipment. At this stage also the bomb doors (which had previously been moulded in with the fuselage shell for ease of manufacture) were cut away from the fuselage moulding and equipped in a separate operation with the necessary hinges and fittings.

The whole of the design had paid attention to the ease of manufacture. One good example of this was the arrangement of the services in the fuselage. Control cables were as far as possible arranged to run on the port side of the fuselage whilst the hydraulic lines ran along the starboard side. In that way most of the systems could be installed before the halves of the fuselage were mated.

The two halves of the fuselage shell had to be clamped together during the final glueing together. The front fuselage was more difficult to hold because of the double curvature, but a fixture was devised which held the halves together firmly. During the assembly of the fuselage, the wing cut-out had to be spanned by a jury-strut in order to prevent distortion taking place. Aft of the wing, the fuselage was held by wooden circular clamps which embraced the section completely. Turnbuckles were used to tighten up these clamps while the glue set.

The mating edges of the fuselage shell had a Vee-shaped projection running all along one side with a corresponding depression on the other edge. These edges were glued together. Plywood butt straps recessed into the skin were added on the inside and outside surfaces to reinforce the joint. These were glued and screwed into position. Once the two halves were joined together, the rest of the internal equipment was then installed into the completed fuselage structure (Fig.28).

The wing was assembled in one piece extending from tip to tip. It was of fairly conventional two-spar design, with chord-wise ribs maintaining the aerodynamic profile. The top skin was load-carrying and consisted of two plywood skins separated and reinforced by closely spaced square-section stringers of Douglas Fir. The bottom skin was similar but with only a single outer skin carrying the stringers - because the compression loads weren't so great in the bottom skins. The tank doors in the bottom skin near the root were balsa sandwich plywood panels.

Fig.28: A Canadian-built fuselage is moved around the factory, whilst in the background a number of shells are in staps while the glue sets. This photograph clearly shows the temporary support rods in the mainplane 'gap' to keep the structure in alignment. (Photo: National Aviation Museum of Canada).

The two spars were of box section. The top and bottom laminated spar booms were connected by two plywood webs located on the forward and aft faces. The top boom was originally made from three laminations of Fir 1.45 inches thick. Because of the problems associated with obtaining timber free from defects to such a thickness, the design was later modified to use a greater number of thinner laminations, which resulted in a weight penalty of only three pounds per aircraft due to the increased area of glued joint. The lower boom was similar but the laminations were only 0.4 of an inch thick.

A special technique had to be developed for sawing these laminations to an accuracy of one hundredth of an inch. One of the advantages which was discovered was that the rough sawn surfaces accepted glue much better than a smoothed surface. So there was a double gain there. The adhesive used in the wing assembly was Beetle glue applied with rubber squeegees. The booms were clamped in special fixtures while the glue was setting. When the glue had set, the booms were taken out and given a final machining to reduce them to the correct dimensions for assembly into the spars and were then jig-drilled for the attachment of later assemblies.

The spar webs were assembled from short lengths of plywood using glued scarfed joints. The whole spar was completed by glueing the webs one at a time to the edges of the booms. At one stage it was found that the glue was taking an awful long time to set. So, under pressure of production, a method was introduced to accelerate the curing by heating them electrically. For the time there was some very subtle monitoring equipment to make sure that the temperature was kept uniform along the length of the spar.

As far as assembly of wing stringers to the skin was concerned, the stringers were first dropped into the slots on a flat table to locate them accurately. The stringers were then attached to the wing skins by screwed and glued joints. Pressure exerted by the screws was adequate to ensure the integrity of the glue joints while the glue cured. After the stringers had been attached to the wing skins, the whole lot was painted with red dope.

The spars were then installed in an assembly jig and the ribs were inserted between them. The ribs were of conventional design with spruce booms and plywood webs. The wing skins were pre-drilled using a template prior to attaching them to the ribs and spars. Incidentally, some 4,000 brass screws were used to assemble each top skin and stringer assembly. Special trolleys were designed to transport the partially completed wings from the build fixtures to final assembly.

After that, the leading edge and shrouds were fitted. The aileron and flap hinges were attached at pre-drilled holes in the rear spar. Shims were used to ensure that the hinge-lines were correctly aligned. The wing was finished off in madapolam fabric and red doped, over which was placed a layer of primer. Finally a coat of camouflage paint was applied. The

electrical and hydraulic systems were then installed in the wing. The fuel tanks were mounted between the spars and the engine mountings bolted in place.

The tail surfaces were just miniature wings. Both had two box spars, which were in effect miniature versions of the wing spars. The tailplane was assembled in a similar jig to that used for the wing.

Each undercarriage leg consisted of two symmetrical 16 SWG sheet steel pressings which were rivetted together along their front and rear edges (Fig.29). In order to ensure that the shock absorbers would have a clear run, a broach-type tool was pulled through the leg after assembly. The shock-absorbers were rubber blocks of an elliptical shape with light alloy spacers between them which fitted into the inner contour of the leg. This simple construction was a production-orientated design as it eliminated any need for accurate machining such as would have been necessary with an oleo unit.

Final assembly was a relatively simple operation. The fuselage was lowered on to the wing centre-section and attached at five points. The complete tail unit was installed on the rear fuselage. The radiators were installed in the leading edge on pre-drilled holes, jig-drilled to ensure interchangeability. The installation of

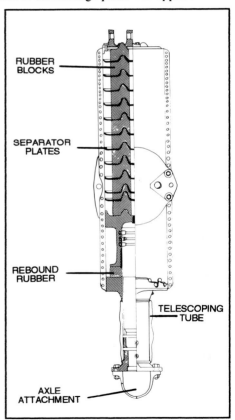

RUBBER BLOCKS

SEPARATOR PLATES

REBOUND RUBBER

TELESCOPING TUBE

AXLE ATTACHMENT

Fig.29: Section of undercarriage leg.

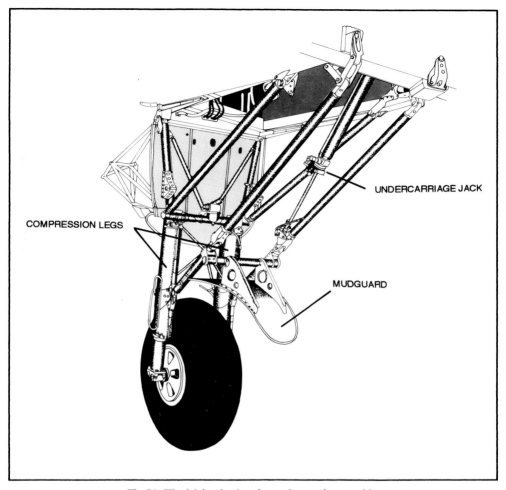

COMPRESSION LEGS

UNDERCARRIAGE JACK

MUDGUARD

Fig 30: The Mainwheel undercarriage unit assembly.

the engines was one of the last operations in the assembly sequence.

The undercarriages were then installed and functioned. I think that the point that Frank made earlier is interesting: for ease of manufacture the aeroplane had been kept as near to the ground as possible during the whole of the assembly process and that meant there wasn't room to operate the undercarriage. To avoid having to jack the aeroplane up to do so, pits were dug in the shop floor at appropriate points, enabling the undercarriage to be lowered and raised without shifting the airframe. After that, all that remained was for the A.I.D. to inspect the aircraft and clear it for delivery to the Royal Air Force.

The operations that I have just described really represent the final system set up for quality production and took several months to establish. Before that stage was reached, de Havilland's had had to adopt a more hand-to-mouth system as the orders received from the

Fig.31: Mosquito assembly, Canadian style. Here 20 aircraft undergo completion on jacks with raised trestles for the engineers at DHC's final assembly shop at Downsview, Toronto. (Photo: National Aviation Museum of Canada)

Ministry very slowly increased in size and complexity.

As we have already heard, the first flight of the Mosquito prototype took place on the 25th November 1940 (Fig.32). Its outstanding performance immediately overcame any remaining opposition in official circles to what was regarded as an unconventional aircraft using outdated production methods. Government orders were soon placed for production in

Fig.32: It flies!. E-0234 returns to earth after its first flight/. (Photo BAe)

limited numbers.

Unfortunately, although the experts were agreed about the superb performance and handling characteristics of the Mosquito, they were far less certain as to what its most useful application as a military machine would be. The first order given to de Havilland's was for 50 aircraft in the bomber and photo-reconnaissance role. In order to obtain an order at all, de Havilland's had to rashly promise to produce the 50 aircraft by December 1941 - which in fact they did not manage to do, but it was the only way to get the order. That was a start, but it was a virtual certainty that a fighter version would be required sooner or later. It was expected from the outset that some of the original order for fifty would be modified to include some fighters. In fact in Government circles there was continual shifting of position regarding the way in which the aircraft ordered should be shared between fighters, bombers and photographic reconnaissance machines.

This indecision had an effect on production. The wings of the fighter version would require stronger manoeuvre load factors for the more agile fighter performance. Accommodation would also have to be provided in the fighters for machine guns and cannon in the fuselage. With great foresight de Havilland's had foreseen what was going to happen, and the basic design of the bomber fuselage had been arranged so as to house those weapons should they be required at a later date (Figs 33 & 34).

Even so, over half the completed bomber fuselages, 28 in all out of the 50, had to have a replacement nose fitted when it was decided at a later date that they were to be delivered as fighters. It was at that stage that some of the advantages of wooden construction made themselves evident - the wooden structure proved much more easy to modify than would

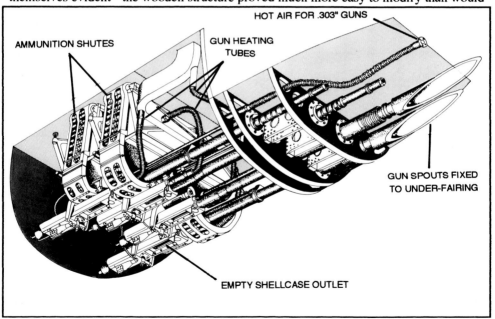

Fig.33: Four 20mm cannon installed under to cockpit of the fighter Mosquito

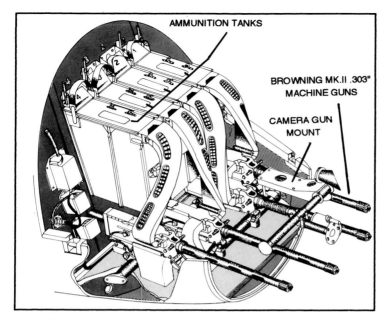

AMMUNITION TANKS

BROWNING MK.II .303"
MACHINE GUNS

CAMERA GUN
MOUNT

Fig.34

Four .303" machine
guns fitted in the
extreme nose of the
Fighter Mosquito.

have been the case with a metal fuselage.

Confidence in the capabilities of the Mosquito had increased so much by the end of 1940 that the first large order was placed for 150 aircraft. Once again, the versions required were not immediately clear. But, by the spring of 1941, it had been decided that all of the 150 aircraft included in the second order should be fighters. At the same time it was promised that another order for 50 fighters would be placed immediately.

At the time that the first orders for the Mosquito were received, de Havilland's were already involved in plans for them to undertake the quantity production of Albermarles - although this was later changed to Wellingtons. Because the rate of production needed was to be 300 aircraft a month, there was no possibility of expanding the Hatfield factory to deal with the demand. In addition, it was obviously advisable to set up a second organization away from Hatfield because of the danger of enemy attacks on the main factory. As a result, when the first evidence became available of the capabilities of the Mosquito, plans were already in hand to set up what was called the Second Aircraft Group to cope with the increased production of Wellingtons.

The new Group was to be located at a shadow factory away from Hatfield and provided with its own airfield. A suitable site had already been chosen at Leavesden near Watford, some ten miles from Hatfield. There was space for a runway of the required length and work was already in progress on the construction of a factory. The de Havilland management now hoped that the Second Aircraft Group would devote its efforts to the manufacture of the Mosquito. Which of course is what happened.

The Mosquito was a unique aircraft insofar as it had been designed to be manufactured not by established organizations in the traditional aircraft industry, but by a large number of companies of all sizes with no previous experience of aircraft manufacture. It did mean however, that these companies had to be quickly trained in the use of aircraft techniques which were unfamiliar to them. They also had to achieve the required standards of interchangeability and to set up inspection techniques of the type required for aircraft production by A.I.D. So, there was quite a lot of work going on in the background to get all that lot set up.

By May 1941, an extensive network of sub-contractors had been set up. Two former furniture manufacturers in High Wycombe, E. Gomme Ltd. and Dancer & Hearne Ltd., were making spars and wings. Vanden Plas in Hendon were making wing coverings. Detail parts were being manufactured by numerous other small companies, including bicycle manufacturers and a firm of craftsmen used to making ecclesiastical ironwork!. Groups of housewives accepted contracts to make simple parts in workshops located in garden sheds, whilst components were being made in garages and church halls.

The task of setting up production in countless small enterprises was a formidable problem for the production planners. Many difficulties were encountered on the way. Some of the plywood was not up to specification. There were, not surprisingly, problems with the quality of some of the glued joints - which are still with us today. The introduction of a new metal aileron caused some difficulties and the production rate of the engine cowlings was causing concern.

The main task of establishing interchangeability standards with agreement from the A.I.D. seems to have been undertaken by Harry Povey, whom lots of us will still remember as the Chief Engineer in charge of production here on the Hatfield site.

As I indicated earlier, throughout the early history of the Mosquito, de Havilland's suffered from a lack of decision from the Ministry as regards the number of aircraft that would be needed. When the decisions arrived they usually were so urgent that the targets set for delivery were almost impossible to achieve - there was no time to plan ahead.

It took a long time to obtain from the Ministry of Aircraft Production a decision as to the total number of the bomber versions which would be needed. It was obvious that sooner or later a further order would be placed for the bomber version but the planning of production was not helped by the delay in arriving at a decision.

By June 1941, the order for fighters had been increased to about 500 aircraft with a production rate of 50 a month. There was still no mention of bombers. By the 10th of July - that was only 6 weeks later - a letter from the Ministry stated that output of 150 Mosquitos a month was required; 80 of them were to be built at Hatfield, 30 were to be produced by the Second Aircraft Group at Leavesden and the other 40 from a new production line to be established in Canada.

It had also been hoped that the United States would build the Mosquito under licence. Early in the flight test programme, the United States Air Force chiefs had been invited to witness a demonstration of the Mosquito and had been very impressed. A complete set of manufacturing drawings was sent over to the States in the hope that the Americans would take the chance to build the Mosquito over there. Five aircraft manufacturing companies in the USA were asked to investigate the information provided by de Havilland's.

I saw in a recently published book on the Mosquito, I haven't seen it before, a reported response from Beech Aircraft, which said: *"It appears that this airplane has sacrificed serviceability, structural strength, ease of construction and flying characteristics in an attempt to use construction material which is not suitable for the manufacture of efficient airplanes".*

The United States Air Force in the First World War had been almost entirely equipped with de Havilland aircraft built under licence. Unfortunately, they rejected the opportunity to repeat the experience a second time.

The firm go-ahead for the production of bombers in quantity finally arrived in the middle of July 1941. Instructions were received that the last 10 of the photographic reconnaissance version and the last 50 of the order for 200 fighters were to be converted to bombers. Even then the decision was slightly tempered by the statement that some forward armament might possibly be needed.

By this time, de Havilland's were finding it difficult to come up with any production planning at all, for the requirements were changing faster than plans could be formulated. Any hope of producing the promised 50 aircraft before the end of 1941 had long been abandoned. In the absence of long term planning it was also becoming increasingly more difficult to order materials. Under pressure from de Havilland's, a letter was obtained from the Contracts Department confirming the need for 150 aircraft a month, including those manufactured in Canada. This enabled orders for raw materials to be placed. A further contract for 400 aircraft was promised.

By August 8th, which was only a couple of months' later, the Ministry asked for the programme to be increased from 150 to 160 aircraft a month with a possibility of a further increase to 200 a month before very long. To accomplish this, it would be necessary to involve other manufacturers.

Then the Ministry decided that full-scale production of bombers was to start in January 1942. By then plans for Mosquito production in Canada were well advanced. The first aircraft (Fig.35) would be compelled to use some imported parts from Britain in the first few months until specialized production facilities could be set up in Canada. The aim was to reach a production rate of 50 aircraft a month by May 1943.

When the decision was made that a bomber version was required in large numbers, the pressure on de Havilland's to step up the produced rate still further became intense. A new programme was prepared calling for 90 fighters a month and 110 bombers a month including

Fig.35: The roll-out of the first Canadia-built Mosquito - KB300. (Photo: National Aviation Museum of Canada)

the Canadian contribution. The total number of Mosquitoes on order now totalled 1,778. As the demand for bombers increased, this figure was soon pushed up to 3,849. It was becoming almost impossible to keep up with the demand.

The total number of armament, radar and engine differences ensured that the picture never remained static for long. There was continual pressure to incorporate these improvements as soon as possible on the production line. By March 1943, there were ten different marks of Mosquito in production plus the special photographic reconnaissance versions.

At the beginning of 1942, plans were formulated for the production of the Mosquito in Australia (Fig.36). It was intended that the first aircraft would fly in August 1943, but because of the lack of engineering resources in Australia, the task proved more difficult than anticipated. As in the case of Canada, many of the materials for the first aircraft had to be imported from Britain. Shipping large quantities from this country in wartime conditions proved difficult. Japanese aircraft sank some of the ships on their way, causing further delays to the planned programme.

Fig.36: A52-41, an Australian-built FB.Mk.40

A further more fundamental problem with Australian production involved the glueing of the wing structure. Doubts were raised about the integrity of a wing joint which was not easy to inspect visually because of its position in the wing to fuselage structure. The Directorate of Aeronautical Inspection felt it necessary to call for the non-destructive testing of all the wings already built. The tests showed the necessity to modify all of the fifty completed wings with a disastrous effect on the programme of deliveries.

By the end of the war in Europe, 108 Mosquitoes had been built in Australia, with production of the Mosquito continuing for some time after that. It was expected that the war with Japan would last for at least another year and the Mosquito was destined for various duties in the Pacific. The dropping of the atomic bombs on Hiroshima and Nagasaki brought an unexpected early end to the war. The total number of Australian Mosquitoes finally reached 212, by which time almost the whole of the basic aircraft was manufactured of Australian materials.

In total, no less than 7,781 Mosquitoes were built. The details of the various orders are given in Martin Sharp's "D.H. An Outline of de Havilland History". The exact numbers actually manufactured are not entirely clear, for some orders were not completed but cancelled before the full complement was manufactured. To the nearest tens, the contributions of the various manufacturing organizations were roughly: Hatfield 3,020, Leavesden 1,750, Standard Motors 1,120, Percival Aircraft 250, Airspeed 410, Chester 100, Canada 1,030 and Australia 210. The last Mosquito to be built was completed at Chester in November 1950.

The final operational flight of an RAF Mosquito, a photo-reconnaissance flight over terrorist bases in Malaya, took place just over five years later on the 15th. December 1955.

Having come to the end, I remember someone once said that if you give someone half a dozen decent slides and a script, you have a lecture - what sorts out the men from the boys is when you get to question time. So, I am hoping that there are people in the audience that can answer better than I questions on Mosquito production details. Thank you".

Discussion.

Mr Tony Saint returned to the podium:

"That was a fascinating exposition Frank - you put such a tremendous amount of detail into such a short space of time. We have just a few minutes for question time".

From the floor: "I was intrigued about the two-halves of the fuselage being put together. How were they fixed? - just by glue or by some bolting?".

Mr Frank Vann: "As I said, one half of the fuselage was ended in a Vee and the other half of the fuselage ended in a Vee-shaped recess fitted together. So the joint was glued and the two were pressed together by these bands around while they set, but in addition, plywood butt straps were placed over the joint, and the butt straps were glued and screwed, so there was a bonded butt joint and also a shear-carrying strip over the joint to make it stronger".

Don Middleton: "This particular form of construction was of course pioneered with the Handley Page Hampden a few years previously and was very successful there. But two aspects of the particular type of Mosquito build - the very smooth rear fuselage produced two problems. One, the difficulty of controlling connubial activity in the rear fuselage on the night-shift; and the second one was the problem of fixing the aft bulk-head which clearly took an enormous load - it took the whole of the tail unit on the pyramidial bracing and at the end of the open fuselage it was formed into, as far as I can remember a parallel formation, and this bulk head which I think is about two inches thick was pushed in and clearly there had to be a good glue joint there but to complicate the issue the rear face of it was plywood and extended about oh I suppose, at least 5/8ths of an inch outboard of the actual rim of it. So, clearly it was essential to have a very close matching joint around those two to get a really good glued finish. There was an occasion when it was discovered by Inspection that several of these bulkheads had been very very carelessly finished and there was a void for about 45% of the periphery of it. Geoffrey de Havilland Jnr - the test pilot - heard about this and was absolutely livid!. He demanded to be able to take the person that was responsible for this appalling mistake up in the aeroplane - Geoffrey would have a parachute and this other guy would not. He was going to do aerobatics until the tail fell off, but a few guys I think persuaded him that this was not the right approach to it".

Mr Tony Saint. "Thank you very much, just one more question now".

From the floor: "Just an additional rider of that remark in fact about the bulkhead. I believe it was called bulkhead G, and there was one little fellow who always wore a cap and his job was to go through this bulkhead to see that all was well at the back side. I don't know his name but he was a little fellow and he was worth his weight in gold!".

Mr Tony Saint took the podium: "Thank you very much indeed Frank. If it helps, from some 40 years on in my lifetime, I was educated by an ex- Handley Page chap at Preston factory where we got the first prototype Jaguar fighter. Lo and behold what did he teach us to put into the slats and the flap vanes but balsa wood construction. That's how we got the first prototype going. So that technique certainly carried on".

CHAPTER SIX

TEST FLYING THE EARLY MOSQUITOES
Speaker - Pat Fillingham

The Chairman Tony Saint took the podium:
"Right, we'll now proceed on to the next speaker. May I introduce - and I'm sure he needs no introduction to most of you - Pat Fillingham".

Pat Fillingham took the podium.
"Ladies, Gentlemen and fellow Members, it is with some reluctance that I stand up to speak to you this afternoon. I don't have to remind you how long ago this epic event took place. After 50 years I have suffered a substantial loss of memory. As an example, I woke up this morning and I could not remember if the Mosquito was a Biplane or a Monoplane! So, if I forget something, or stammer and stutter - which I will - then please forgive me.

Let me set the scene - Hatfield in 1940 was a grass field, two thirds of its present size. No runways, no radio, no R/T, no Met - we just landed into wind. There was a controller who sat in a small hut with a Very pistol and an Aldis lamp - red and green to give landing clearance. We had just four Test Pilots at Hatfield - the Chief, Geoffrey de Havilland Jnr (son of Sir Geoffrey), George Gibbins, John de Havilland (Sir Geoffrey's youngest son), and myself.

You may be interested to know that we started test flying Tigers at £175 a year. If you behaved and did well, after 6 months your salary was doubled to £350 per annum, then you went onto the Oxford and paid some Income Tax! Of course we had clothes and food rationing, but £7 per week was a princely sum. You could get digs 30 bob; buy a good second - hand car for £20; and petrol was about a shilling a gallon - and woe betide you if you were caught with aviation fuel in your motor car tank. But it must be said, you had to have a private income to work for de Havilland's!. It was all good fun.

We were testing Tiger Moths, Airspeed Oxfords, Rapides, Masters and some Hurricanes. The Hurricanes were slightly damaged 'Fly Ins' from the Battle of Britain and after a quick turnaround for repairs we gave them a 30 minute flight and they went back to their Squadrons. About this time we were given the chance to fly some fast aircraft. I remember flying a Boston, a Westland Whirlwind with two Peregrines and we had a Mew Gull in for aileron assessment, which we found extremely light and responsive.

As for the Mosquito, there was great excitement when the prototype arrived at the main gate - the fuselage on one lorry and the wing on another to be re-assembled in an old paint shop at the far end of the factory (Fig. 37). After two weeks it was out for engine runs and on the 25th November, Geoffrey de H and John Walker - the Chief Engine Development Engineer - a pilot in his own right and a great friend of mine, taxied out onto the airfield. They did a short hop about a foot or so off the ground, then taxied back to check the glycol coolant as there was some slight overheating. As all was well they then took off in a very short distance, the gear was retracted, and they flew for about 30 minutes, reaching a speed of about

Fig.37: E-0234 (later to be serialed W4050) is prepared in a protected hardstand at Hatfield during November 1940. The covers are on to prevent the aircraft's bright yellow colour scheme from being spotted by prowling German aircraft. (Photo: BAe)

230 m.p.h before coming in for a good landing. All was very satisfactory.

After a few flights it became obvious that the aircraft was extremely manoeuvrable. Geoffrey de H did some spectacular demonstrations for the Ministry and the Air Force (Fig.38). One big feature was the vapour trails formed at the wingtips under high 'G'. which, when the aircraft passed you by, you could hear the crackle of the air as it closed up. This phenomenon soon became known as 'Audible Vortices'.

On one of these flights Mr R.E Bishop, our Chief Designer went aloft. At the end of this flight the undercarriage would not come down, so Bish - as he was known to us - had to use the emergency system. This involved pumping on an emergency pump and after some 300 pumps the undercarriage was still not down and they ran out of hydraulic fluid. Luckily the last 200 pumps were on air and the gear was locked down. That night there were some changes in the design office!.

The first problem to arise was buffet on the tailplane. It was caused by a bad airflow from the engine nacelles. Wool tufts were stuck on with 'Bostik' to show the flow pattern. Now I see in my log-book for December 9th 1940 that I "Flew Hurricane P3090 - observing the air-flow tufts on the DH Mosquito at various speeds". So that was 2 weeks' after the first flight. - this problem was finally cured by extending the engine nacelles. However, because of this the flaps had to be split.

In the early summer of 1941, both John de H and I went solo on the Mosquito. I well remember my flight - there were no pilots' notes, I was given 5 minutes instruction in the

Fig.38: Now painted as W4050, the prototype moves out to the runway at Hatfield during the manufacturer's trials. (Photo: BAe)

cockpit, told "...to put the tail trim one division forward and land at 120 m.p.h.. Watch the swing and don't go too far away!". I enjoyed that flight, made an approach over the factory and landed safely.

The Mosquito undercarriage was very good - rubber in compression. I was taught in the Technical School that you cannot compress rubber - only distort it - so it was always 'rubber in distortion 'for me.

As is well documented, Geoffrey de Havilland flew the second aircraft - a fighter - out of the field adjacent to Salisbury Hall (Fig.39). George Gibbins flew the third out in a similar way. At this time there was an attempt to disfigure the Mosquito by fitting a gun turret and an umbrella-type airbrake (Fig. 40). These produced too much drag and luckily they were dropped and not seen again.

Now, electrics. Electrics were mistrusted by all pilots at that date - they were always a problem. Indeed, the early Mosquito only had one generator - on the port side, I think, so if you lost that engine you had to rely on the battery and its amps for all the electrical services. The early Mosquitoes went to the Services with only one generator, but the RAF soon stipulated two. There is a story of crossed wires in that when the Nightshift Foreman at Hatfield turned on the hangar lights, one of the Mosquitoes started up!

Then the aircraft went to Boscombe Down to be checked. The pilots were very impressed and the top speed turned out to be I think, 10 mph above the Spitfire. Boscombe was a very rough and hilly field with no runways in those days, and unfortunately the tailwheel caught in a rut and cracked the fuselage above the rear door. Hatfield quickly came up with a repair scheme and a strake appeared on the starboard fuselage above the rear door. Every Mosquito built carries this strake and it is hardly noticeable.

So when production started we produced a flight-test schedule. It was a long roll of paper fitted to your knee-pad with all the gen being written on it. I'll quickly run through a typical first flight.

After take-off, you took all the figures on the climb, went up to 15,000ft. Check the

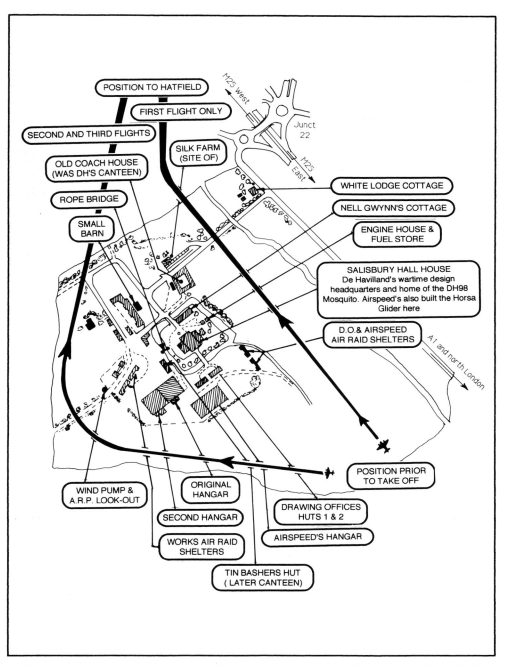

POSITION TO HATFIELD

FIRST FLIGHT ONLY

M25 West

M25 East

Junct 22

SECOND AND THIRD FLIGHTS

SILK FARM
(SITE OF)

OLD COACH HOUSE
(WAS DH'S CANTEEN)

ROPE BRIDGE

SMALL
BARN

WHITE LODGE COTTAGE

NELL GWYNN'S COTTAGE

ENGINE HOUSE &
FUEL STORE

SALISBURY HALL HOUSE
De Havilland's wartime design
headquarters and home of the DH98
Mosquito. Airspeed's also built the Horsa
Glider here

D.O.& AIRSPEED
AIR RAID SHELTERS

A1 and north London

POSITION PRIOR
TO TAKE OFF

WIND PUMP &
A.R.P. LOOK-OUT

ORIGINAL
HANGAR

SECOND HANGAR

DRAWING OFFICES
HUTS 1 & 2

AIRSPEED'S HANGAR

WORKS AIR RAID
SHELTERS

TIN BASHERS HUT
(LATER CANTEEN)

Fig.39: Sketch map showing the area, and direction of the Mosquito flights from Salisbury Hall.
Based on a drawing by Alan H. Copas.

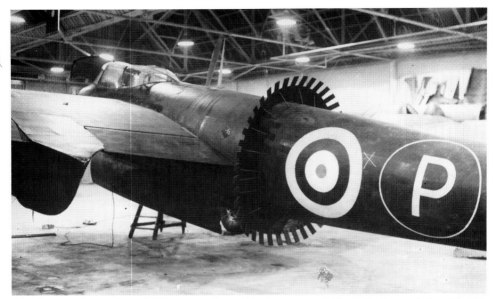

Fig.40: One of a number of different versions of the Youngman Frill Air Brake as tried on W4052 when the aircraft was at Salisbury Hall. (Photo: BAe)

supercharger change over into high gear - up to 30,000ft to check pressure venting. Drop down to rated altitude and did some level speeds, then down to 15,000 to do the stalls. The stall was absolutely first class. It was caused of course by the radiators being inboard of the engines and next to the fuselage and it gave you a perfect wing-root stall. There was never any trouble with the stall.

A few aerobatics were done to test the ailerons, a dive to the VNE to check the stick forces and the tailplane incidence and then in to land. This took about 50 minutes to an hour. Then we did a second flight of about 20 minutes to check snags. And a third flight of 10 minutes and the aircraft was off test. Sometimes we had an aeroplane with no snags at all and this was called 'A Lulu' - one with a lot of snags was called 'A Rogue".

We attached great importance to good ailerons. You could shim them up or down; gear the tabs; put on droop, take it off and, in desperation, you could change the complete aileron, much to the disgust of the Works Manager. However, you had to watch for over-balance at low speeds.

Now, as far as I know there was no spinning done on Mosquitoes and in the early days very little was known about compressibility. Geoffrey de Havilland did go to the States to discuss the subject in late 1942 with senior American pilots. That was production testing and at one stage, I think we did 33 aeroplanes per week.

Now the weather!! As we had no radio and no Met, the weather was a huge problem. The chief trouble was fog, for there was no smokeless fuel during the War, and on one bad February we had over 100 aeroplanes on the field awaiting test. We would fly to the northwest when clear of the Chilterns, climb up and return on the reciprocal for the let-down and use the railway lines to get you back to Hatfield. This was known as 'Bradshawing' after the well known railway timetable of that era.

I recall a very long flight over cloud with a new observer - it was his first flight. We went up to 30,000ft and did several level checks and were up a long time. When we came down, we broke cloud at about 1,000ft but it was very misty so we flew along low to see what we could pick-up. The first thing we saw was three giraffes in a field. I turned to the observer and said, "Strong tail wind, we must be over Africa". He paled. We were of course over the zoo at Whipsnade, just a short trip back to Hatfield.

Another time on a foggy day we went down to the cinema at Hatfield to see a film, I think it was a Western - in black and white. We sat in the 1/9s in the front, and halfway through the film the screen went blank to be replaced with a printed notice on the screen, "The weather has cleared, will the de Havilland pilots please go back to work". Well, we went back, but of course it hadn't cleared, and you could not even see the Main Gate. The Works Manager got his own back, but I still remember Jock Allardyce with great affection.

I was lucky to be sent to Canada to set up the Production there at the de Havilland Plant at Toronto. To my horror I was sent up to Liverpool and put on a ship to cross the North Atlantic in the depths of winter. I well remember its name, it was the 'Empress of Japan' - not a good omen! It was full of Air Force personnel and four of us civilians. We were not allowed to undress at night and wore life-jackets all day. There was also a rota for U-Boat spotting - I for one saw at least 50 imaginary periscopes!. We went flat out across the Atlantic, zig-zagging all the way and arrived safely at Halifax, Nova-Scotia. I have never been on a boat since!

The Canadian aeroplanes were very good (Fig.41). We had some minor troubles with the fuel injection system on the Packard-built Merlins, which had a tendency to ice up. Whilst in Canada, I took a Mosquito to Colorado Springs for the Americans to check. The English accent caused some amusement to them, and why do we call the gear 'the chassis?' - all the

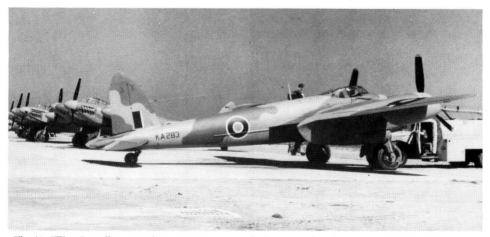

Fig.41: "The Canadian aeroplanes were very good..." A row of six brand new FB.Mk.26's on the flightline at Downsview with KA283 in the foreground. (Photo: National Aviation Museum of Canada).

Mosquitoes used this extraordinary word, and why Punka Louvre for the air vent?. Perhaps we had some retired Indian Colonel in the Drawing Office.!! One morning I went into the Hangar and under each wingtip was a pile of sawdust with a placard saying, 'Termites at work'. But the performance of the aeroplane was no laughing matter, they were most impressed.

I was sent on to Sydney Australia to start Production there. Six of us went in the bomb-bay of a Liberator, each had a seat and a light. We went via San Francisco, Hawaii, Canton Island and on to Brisbane. I spent most of my time expecting the bomb doors to open! When in Sydney I tried to pluck up courage to fly under the Sydney Harbour Bridge, but I never made it.

On my way home I was asked to fly a Mosquito from Montreal to the United Kingdom, via the short route, that's Goose Bay, Greenland, Iceland and Prestwick. There had been several unexplained losses on the Ferry route from Canada. The trip from Goose to Greenland is quite spectacular at the entry to the Fjiord. Before you go, you are shown a film, of the entry to the Fjiord with a commentary. Turn left at the first wreck, right at the next intersection (the left one is the dead end), right again at the big iceberg and when you see the airfield, land straight ahead - no circuits were allowed. We were given R/T, ADF and of all

Fig.42: The drivers position. The pilots panel of a B.Mk.IV. From the sight of the tools and panels removed on the right hand side of the picture, it appears that the aircraft was undergoing servicing at the time!. (Photo: BAe)

things, a sextant, Neither my Canadian Navigator or myself would admit that we could not work a sextant. When we arrived at the entrance to the Fjiord after an 800 mile flight from Goose Bay, we discovered that there was cloud cover at 1,000ft. Halfway up the Fjiord we were in R/T touch with the airfield and were told to return to base as the weather was too bad to land. So I pulled up through the cloud and did a quick 180 and headed back to Goose 800 miles away. The cloud tops were only 3,000ft but we still picked up a lot of ice in a very short time. We landed at Goose at night after some six hours in the air and still with adequate fuel. I firmly believe the Ferry losses were due to ice, for the Mosquito had no airframe anticing or deicing.

All in all we tested 3,300 Mosquitoes at Hatfield and 1,500 at Leavesden. I was lucky I only had one serious incident. During a climb to 30,000ft my observer passed out at about 23,000ft, I remember looking at him and thinking 'the fool'. I let down a thousand or so feet, checked the oxygen indicator (which showed that it was flowing) so I climbed up again. Then I decided to go down. I put the oxygen to emergency and felt the flow on my face - also the regulator showed it was working. Luckily as I descended, my observer came to and we landed with splitting headaches. It was later found that the oxygen system was filled with compressed air. Connectors were subsequently changed and you can now no longer fit a compressed air bottle to an oxygen system. Anoxia is a very strange experience.

So ladies and gentlemen I was lucky to test the finest aeroplane of its day; it was also the fastest and had a remarkable range and load carrying capacity. With beautifully balanced controls it was easy to fly and became part of you when you were airborne. Finally ladies and gentlemen, if anyone would like to ask a question I will do my best".

Discussion

Desmond Penrose: "You mentioned the ailerons on the Mew Gull which interested me, but I am particularly interested to know when you said that the Mosquito was a fine handling machine, how you thought it compared with the Hornet. After all, it was a later and a slightly more aerodynamic looking machine...?"

Pat Fillingham: "The Hornet was of course faster than the Mosquito, but it had spring balanced ailerons which were the cause of great trouble. It wasn't as good an aeroplane as the Mosquito was. It was a little nose heavy, so it was not easy to land properly".

Frank Armstrong RAE: "A mention has been made of the performance of the Mosquito in terms of speed and the rate of climb and so forth. How did it really rate in terms of dog-fighting capability against the single engine types? Did it have similar rates of roll and that sort of thing? Was it really an effective dog-fighter? - Or would it have been had there been a real demand for that sort of thing, in the era of the service of Mosquito?".

Pat Fillingham:"Well, I am going to find that very difficult to answer because I really don't know. It wasn't a thing we tried out at Hatfield because I was mainly concerned with Production. But I know there was some changing of the balance weight which hung below the stick, and I believe some Squadrons had this balance weight increased in weight, but what they actually fitted was a balsa one".

Tom Summerville, ex Aerodynamics Dept. RAE Farnborough: "On a spot of history of the events following the first flight of the aircraft. You suggested that the aircraft had those wool tufts on it. After that flight both Mr Clarkson and Mr Bishop came down to the Aerodynamics Department of the RAE to discuss what we could do with regards to improving the separation from the nacelle. We developed a wind tunnel model within a couple of weeks and also tested the aircraft within the following two weeks, after which it was suggested the modification was to extend on the nacelle, which subsequently went into production. At that time we also improved the intakes and perhaps on the question this morning about the relationship between the Westland Whirlwind and the de Havilland aircraft. The actual design of those intakes was in fact taken from the Whirlwind wind tunnel model which had been tested in the large wind tunnel a year earlier. The eventual result was to increase the top speed of the aircraft by about nine miles an hour".

Air Vice Marshal Gill:"On the penultimate question I could probably throw a little light. I was converted onto Mk. VI Mosquitoes by a Flt Lt Porter. His remark was "...these will do all that the P-51 will do and what's more they do it on one!". He went up in a T.III and it did in fact do it - it took up a bit more sky, but it would do it!. Much later, following the war, at Fasberg there was a wing of Tempest 2s. We did not know at the time, but these pilots got brownie points if they got a shot up the backside of one of the Mk VIs which were at Gutersloh. We later discovered that they got these extra Mars Bars if they got the shot and our approach was to get about 5,000ft in height on them, come down fairly gently (they were slightly better in speed than we were on the level), then feather a prop and go past them on one - they lost all interest!".

Tony Saint returned to the podium: "That was a great ending to a fascinating session. Thank you very much".

CHAPTER SEVEN

EVOLUTION
Speaker - Michael J Bowyer

Tony Saint as Chairman took the stand:
"We now move back again to Michael Bowyer, who will now take us through some of the marks and variants in development of the Mosquito".

Mr Michael Bowyer took the podium.
"While having lunch today, someone came up to me and said 'The worst thing you can do if you give a talk or a lecture is to start the whole day's show'. I think the worst thing to have to do now is to follow Pat Fillingham, because he's told some really superb stories. However, I can recall one or two things that happened to me when I used to come to Hatfield while doing the Mossie book. I hadn't been coming very long, when I wrote a letter to somebody and spelt Mosquitoes without an 'e'. I gather that around here that was almost a criminal offence. So I now spend my time looking at other people's books, and smile when I see they don't spell it 'oes' at the end!.

I am going to consider in the next few minutes the way in which the Mosquito developed during the war for a number of roles, and perhaps make one or two observations about Mosquitoes that are not generally known. I will start with the reconnaissance versions, then go on to cover the bomber and fighter variants.

First of all, let us remind ourselves of the aeroplanes that preceeded the Mosquito. First was the superb de Havilland Comet, which has been mentioned so many times today. That was followed by the Albatross Airliner. If you look at the two aeroplanes you can, I think, see a similarity in line and, with some imagination when you reach the Mosquito well, it's an overgrown Albatross of a sort. In between comes the unexpected de Havilland metal airliner, the Flamingo, before we come to the aeroplane we are talking about today.

The decision to go ahead with a reconnaissance Mosquito (Fig.43) was finally taken in December 1940 - to be precise on the 14th of December - at a meeting between officials of Air Ministry and the Ministry of Aircraft Production. They decided that for a start they would go for twenty P.R. Mossies. Already the decision had been officially taken to have Fighters, and we heard from Frank Vann how frequently the Production Programme changed and how complicated it became in the end with Fighters, Bombers and PR Aircraft being interwoven on the production lines.

The idea in 1940 was to consider an aeroplane to replace the Bristol Blenheim in the PRU and which would have a top speed of about 384mph and an all up-weight of a little over 19,000lb. But one thing is quite obvious, if you are going to run a reconnaissance unit what are you going to reconnoitre? To use Mosquitoes on short range reconnaissance over France didn't really make sense but to use them for longer range purposes up to the Norwegian coast did (and particularly to the north Norwegian area round Narvik, where the Germans exported iron ore along the coast from the ice-free port) where Germans ships likely to be operating in

Fig.43: The prototype Photogrpahic Reconnaissance Mosquito, W4051 undergoing ground runs. Note the small exhaust shrouds and 'doughnut tailwheel, which was later changed to the double-track type to avoid tailwheel 'shimmy'. (Photo: BAe)

the Atlantic would make their escape, this was an area that should come under surveillance. This was best done from Scotland - so the Mosquitoes operated from Wick.

Where else might the enemy effort be necessary to survey in great detail? Well of course, obviously deep into Germany. But risking those early Mosquitoes on such flights had to be thought about, so another area was chosen for surveillance, Biscay. One thing was obvious; the Mosquito was not yet operating at its very best, a lot more mileage was to come. The first major change was the increase to the fuel load - carry the extra fuel and then the aircraft would have great use in the Middle East.

There was an aeroplane that had done brilliantly in the Middle East War, an unexpected machine, the American-built Glen Martin Maryland. When the RAF received the first Marylands, they weren't quite sure what to do with them, for although not very well armed defensively, they were quite fast and had superb range - one did a 10 hour trip out of Malta during the Battle of Britain. So here was the answer to it, a very fast one, a vastly superior aeroplane that was able to fly higher, which could look at Italy and could look far in the Middle East. Of course, the Mosquito eventually would also play an important role in the Far East War.

In the middle of those ideas for a change, came a decision that some of the Mosquitoes, after all, would be completed as bombers on an experimental basis. So the first twenty became half PR aircraft and half bomber aircraft. Of course the point has to be made, that basically the airframe was the same throughout the war, except that some of the aircraft would have to be strengthened, and some would have various refinements. But basically it would be the same airframe. Most amazing of all, there would be 43 different marks of Mosquito (Fig.44). We can recall a Seafire 47, for instance, but there weren't 47 actual designs of 'Spitfire'; there were a lot and nearly that number, but there were 43 actual designs of Mosquito - a few of which didn't emerge, and because the particular requirement was not worth pursuing.

One of the first changes that had to come, and we heard about it this morning, in that very detailed talk about the Merlin from Alec Harvey-Bailey, was to fit the Merlin 61, the two-stage engine into a Mosquito. The reason for that was simply that the Air Force believed that with the Focke-Wulf 190 coming into service, they would have to fly a good bit higher. There was no doubt about it. Yet there was an irony in all of this, for in the British operational sphere the 190 quite often attacked at low level, particularly along the South Coast. In the middle of the war there was a perceptible change where Fighters and Fighter-Bombers would go in low and this change came roughly at the time when the Merlin 61 was going into the prototype Mosquito.

But as a reconnaissance aircraft, the Merlin 61 powered machine obviously had great advantages. You could get higher and could go further if you had the extra fuel, which you would need for that engine. Eventually it was decided also to supplement those first 10 P.R. aircraft with another 26 converted Mosquitoes.

In the meantime the decision had been made that the company should develop a Bomber - a dedicated Bomber - which was the Mosquito V.

Well now, around about the middle of '43 (in fact the Spring of '43) there were some major conferences with Bomber Command at Air Ministry level in London as to what should be done with the two-stage Merlin Mosquito, designated the Mark IX. The initial decision was made that it had very little use in Bomber Command, for it didn't fit the existing programme. Plans had been made for a heavy bomber force - with Lancasters and Halifaxes. Then quite out of the blue came the realization that this little aeroplane could do something else as well as take photographs; it could carry highly specialized equipment which we haven't yet heard of yet today, and that was 'Oboe'.

When this radio device, rather like the German Knickebein and X-Gerät was applied to the Mosquito, it could be despatched with great precision to a small target - to find, mark and attack it. The higher the aircraft flew the better, for then it could receive the necessary transmissions from the U.K at a greater range. Therefore a few of the twin-stage engine Mosquitoes would after all be sent to 109 and 105 Squadrons, would be diverted to bombing and using the 'Oboe' device rather than all be used for P.R. purposes.

Another application of the reconnaissance version had a spin-off to the Bomber, and that was the pressure cabin version which appeared in the middle of August 1942. That meant that the Mosquito could operate at 40,000ft, and make lone reconnaissance flights. It also gave a greater element of safety. One could go further, but by the time that the pressure cabin aircraft was in use, the German jets and the Me 163's were available to pick-off a lone flyer that was leaving a contrail perhaps, or if he had not got high enough.

Finally in the search for a good reconnaissance aircraft to get higher to defeat the Germans jets it needed became a lighter machine. It had a greater span, just to give it that

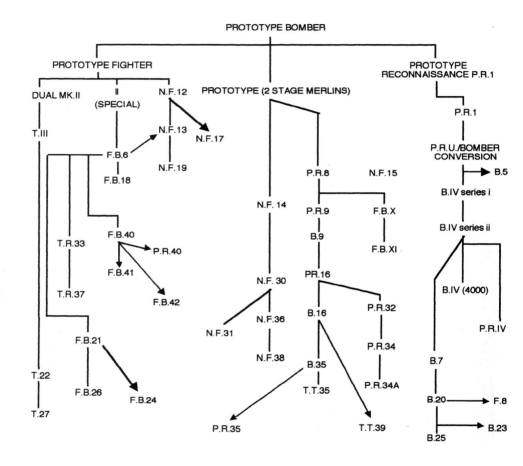

Fig.44: Geneology of the Mosquito

extra capability at high altitude. This was the PR 32, of which there were 5 made, and they were used during the end of the war - particularly to survey German railways.

If you are going to operate an aeroplane like the Mosquito in the Far East, (irrespective of the merits or otherwise of the wooden construction which I am not going into) then the distances to be flown are enormous. So we see a Mosquito fitted with an extended bomb bay - which would normally have carried a very large bomb - a 4,000 pounder. In this case it is crammed with fuel (Fig.45). Not only has it a lot of fuel there, it has wing points for carrying gigantic tanks, up to 200 gallons in each, although that sort of thing was not operationally desirable because of the weight of it, but it could be used for ferry purposes. Because of the distances involved, the aircraft's fuel capacity had gone up from 700 gallons to 1,269 gallons, giving a range of 3,600 miles at 25,000ft. The weight of course had risen dramatically, from 19,000 to about 25,500 pounds.

Fig.45: Long-range fuel tanks in the bomb bay. These would give the later marks of P.R. machines a range of over nine hours. (Photo: BAe)

Some of those Mosquitoes evidently suffered the same fate as one in the hanger here, because there were many stories that went round after the War of termites eating Mosquitoes. I knew someone who swore to me that his aeroplane had virtually disappeared overnight. So we know where Pat Fillingham's termites went - out East!

The first Mosquito built was neither Bomber nor Fighter, it was a research aircraft. But it looked like a Bomber, and it behaved like the Bomber. The eighth Mosquito - W4057 - which first flew in September '41 turned out to be the first of the Bombers. It not until July '41 that the decision had been made to go ahead with Bombers. What immediately improved the aircraft (as we heard this morning) was the decision that it must carry a bigger load, achieved by cropping the vanes of 500lb bombs and fitting four in. That was a most unpopular thing to do, and at Boscombe Down, it was said,"We don't want other people interfering with bombs, we do that sort of thing. It's not for civilians to do it". de Havillands turned round and said," Well, it works very well, doesn't it?" C. T. Wilkins' plan showed that the Mosquito could carry twice the load that anyone had envisaged. It could also have Merlin 61s, and the Bomber version with those would get just as high as reconnaissance aircraft.

But it wasn't really as simple as that when on the 31st of May 1942, 105 Squadron at Horsham St Faith put the Mosquito into operational service, as a Bomber. The first flights of course, had been made by the PR aircraft, the previous September, so people knew quite a bit about flying them over enemy territory.

These Mosquitoes were precious, they had to be looked after. But after the 'thousand bomber' raid on Cologne, Bomber Command ordered that the Mosquitoes should have a look to see what had happened. When the first one got there the city was burning and there was nothing to see except smoke. By 8 o' clock in the morning when the next one went, the weather was not too good, it was hazy and there was still a mass of smoke. Not one of the four that had gone by mid-afternoon found evidence as to what had happened, except that the city had received a most ghastly torture.

The last to go was Squadron Leader Channer who said, "Well, I'll go lower". By going lower, as one looks back from a historical point of view, one sees that would be the first time the Mosquito had been used in a totally different role from than for which it was envisaged. The original idea was tried out in early September '42, against Berlin in day-light. Thus the aircraft would make a flight over enemy territory very high and fast, drop its bombs on a precision target, and come back. But now they had tried that, they had flown high, and in the weeks after the Cologne raid there were lots of attempts to use the Mosquito in a conventional role while going quite high, taking photographs, dropping bombs, on places like Essen, Bremen and Hamburg. But if you went low you went below the radar, you were difficult to detect. If you flew a dog-leg track then you were going to be even more difficult to detect. And if you flew out at sea for part of the way as happened on the first raid on Flensburg, then you would be far less vulnerable to any enemy interference. So the tactics employed began to be vitally important for the success of the Mosquito.

It was also discovered that one could have two types of attack; low level and shallow dive; with the shallow dive perhaps preceding the low level raid. By attacking at dusk or late in the afternoon, you had another tactical ploy which was well worth exploring - out by day-light and back by dark. But it has to be said, to be fair, that the loss rate was still quite high with the Mosquitoes; in fact sometimes as high as 10%. There is no good glossing over the fact that it was a hazardous thing to do - to go in daylight.

Another important thing was that if you could add more fuel as for the P.R. versions - could you alternatively add more bombs? Well of course you could. You could add them on the wings.

The type that made the Cologne raid to be precise was a PR conversion. If you can fit something under the wing - a drop tank - you can extend the range (Fig.46). But if you don't do that, you could possibly improve the offensive load, you could have bombs on the wings (Fig.47 & 48). That was done with the B IXs. One could also swell the bomb bay underneath - it could then carry a bigger bomb, even a 4,000 pounder. The realization that the aircraft could take a far greater load was most important for its future.

The productive effort of one Mosquito against a German target at night would be much increased, and where its loss rate was extremely low, perhaps .2 or .3%. It would be possible for one aeroplane to deliver an 8,000lb load in one night over two trips. That meant one

Top - Fig.46: 'If you can fit something under the wing...' Here a Mk.XVIII shows the business end of the Molins 57mm cannon and a pair of tanks under the wings to extend the range.

Centre - Fig.47: RF957, a Mk.VI of 45 Sqn shows the under-wing bomb carrier.

Bottom - Fig.48: Another alternative - eight 60lb rockets under the wings together with the normal armament give this Mk.VI tremendous fire-power

Mosquito, as happened quite a number of times at Bourn in Cambridgeshire for instance, flew two trips in a night, with impunity. I remember one pilot saying to me "What I always aimed to do was get the Daily Telegraph cross-word puzzle done on the return trip". That shows both considerable courage and trust in reliability!.

I've just been doing a lot of research work on bomber loads, and I was surprised to find that during 1942 the Lancasters and the Halifaxes were not carrying very heavy bomb loads. The overall bomb load of the Lancaster throughout the war was somewhere around 9,500lb perhaps 10,000 - if one considered them all.

Of course, we have also heard that in the Far East, again this aircraft carried either more fuel or it carried more bombs. But with Merlin 100 series engines it had a better all-round performance. In fact I was looking at several performance ratings the other day, when I was thinking about talking here, and I found that it seemed that on average a Mossie 35 intended for the Far East War was doing 422mph at 30,000ft. That really was going great-guns.

And what about the other main type of Mosquito, the Fighter? Well, the first fighter was ordered at the height of the Battle of Britain. In fact the decision was made, in the Ministry, to order it on the 18th of July 1940. It would have four cannon, four machine guns and would need a different canopy, but nevertheless it would be a very similar aeroplane.

What deeply shocked the Establishment and the Services was the loss, during the height of the Battle of Britain, of the giant liner the *'Empress of Britain'* , quite near to British shores. The Hurricanes and Spitfires didn't have the range to protect ships coming in from the Western Atlantic. A lot of those ships were bringing food, and Lord Woolton pressed for an aeroplane that could protect the ships on the last leg in from the Atlantic. Some suggested a B-24 Liberator with a composite Hurricane on the top. A nice idea - a lot of work was done on it, but it wasn't really viable. No, the best thing was a long range aeroplane, or better, one with a long duration - which was just what the Mosquito had, and that did more for the Mosquito Fighter than the idea that it should fly and fight at night. Of course I am sure we shall hear from John Cunningham about its use as a night-fighter, which was totally outstanding, especially when it was wedded to very sophisticated radar, to narrow beam radar, that could pick out the German Bomber readily.

There was in the meantime an idea that some of the aircraft - the early ones - should be completed as dual control trainers because some said the Mosquito wasn't all that easy to fly. So some of the very early aircraft rather surprisingly appeared as aeroplanes for a pilot and a trainee pilot.

But what was true of the Bombers was also true of the Fighters. Behind the cannon there was room for bombs, two bombs underneath the wings as well, four bombs immediately, four 250 pounders and if necessary, two 500 pounders with cropped tails behind the cannon. That led to the Mark VI which we have already heard about. A remarkable aeroplane. But it also led to an interim version, the Mk.II intruder aircraft, which was used first over Northern Europe and then from Malta.

I remember Sir Peter Wykeham, who was with 23 Squadron and later Vice-Chief of Air Staff (Training) telling me, that one night when they set off from Malta, he said to his Navigator, "We're going to do some train-busting: can you see any trains?" Eventually they found a train somewhere near Foggia, so he said," You know, if we fire at that train it's going to have a lot of sparks and then things happen". They found a train, fired at the engine. But they didn't realize what had happened until the next day, when one of their friends came back and said," There's a lot of trouble on the line at Foggia. You know that engine you fired at? Well, you fired at the wheels, you've melted the wheels, and they've stuck to the track". That was a part of the Mosquito concept that I don't think anybody planned for!

Finally, there's another type of Mosquito we ought to mention today because it was so specialised and precious. I know there are the lovely drawings of the 101 and 102 in the book, and you'll say, "Oh he's missed out the so-and-so", but it's a huge topic isn't it?. I think something should be said about the Mosquito Airliner (Fig. 49) from a company that built such splendid airliners and continues to.

The first Mosquito to be used as a passenger transport was devised at the end of 1942. BOAC were operating Dakotas on the run from Leuchars to Bromma in Sweden. They said "Is there any possibility that you could adapt a Mosquito to carry very important people?" Well, it was not very easy - there wasn't much room in a Mosquito, but it could be done

Fig.49 (above and below) two views of G-AGFV, one of the 'Mosquito Airliners' used by British Overseas Airways Corporation. Note how the civilian registration is underlined in red, white and blue to aid identification. (Photo's: BAe)

although it would be an uncomfortable ride. Whoever travelled as passenger would have to be in the bomb-bay. He would lie on a mattress and have a reading lamp, but he'd be closed in, wouldn't be able to move, he'd have to just lie there praying that all was well. Communication with the cockpit would be just a few code words - he wouldn't be able to have a sensible conversation with anybody from fear the enemy would hear him.

In one case a Mosquito made three passenger trips in a night, well three journeys, one out, back, and out again. I think I am right in saying that the last operation by a Mosquito in the European theatre of war was a flight by a BOAC one. By the end there had been an amazing 520 round trips and only four aircraft lost.

Who did they carry? This was always a great source of fascination. One undoubtedly, was a man we all knew, many of you I'm sure would have thought him quite 'a character' (which he was) - Sir Malcolm Sargeant. What was he doing in the bomb-bay of a Mosquito?. He certainly was not playing a piano or anything! Was he spying? Well the story went round he was, but nobody really knew. There was another very exciting case when someone said "...there's another guy in the bomb-bay tonight and he doesn't speak English, he must be spying the other way!" It turned out he was Marshal Timoshenko, the Russian Military Leader.

How often one sees people who had something to do with Mosquitoes. There is one person that perhaps you didn't know had some Mosquito links, and that is that lady in the T.V series 'All Creatures Great And Small", Tricky Woo's mistress. Margaretta Scott was married to John Wooldridge, who was the leader of 105 during the famous Mosquito day raids.

There are a host of names that one could mention, so many people, and I do hope that when we go home we'll give a thought to them all. Many of them, like John Wooldridge, are no longer with us .

Fig.50: The classic lines of a Mosquito in flight. Here is shown ML991, a B.Mk.XVI. Note the extended lines of the bulged 4,000lb bomb-bay and the wing-mounted tanks.

Discussion

Tony Saint took the Podium: "Thank you Michael just two or three questions if we could please"

John Hellings: " Why did the fighter need a new canopy? It had the flat windscreen which, on the face of it does not seem quite so aerodynamic. Was it something to do with weapon aiming?"

Mike Bowyer: "I think it was much easier for the two people sitting side by side to have a better view ahead. I'm sure that the view was not that bad with the Vee-shaped windscreen, but as I understand it the flat windscreen gave a better view for operations - perhaps you could ask John Cunningham or Pat Fillingham. I know if one sat in one (and I sat in many different machines) I always used to think that it was much easier to see forward with the flat screen".

Ray Simpson: " Can you verify why the second prototype flying from Salisbury Hall was definitely flown from there with the hedges and trees knocked down rather than the first? I have heard lots of stories about it..."

Mike Bowyer: "That's a good question!. I honestly do not know why they flew the second prototype from there - I just don't know, it's a question I have often asked myself. Can anyone tell us?".

Wilf Joyce: "The story as I understand it was that Fred Plumb, the manager of Salisbury Hall, was running a long way behind programme. He got Geoffrey there one day and said "Can you go out of the field?". He said "Yes, I'll go out of the field if you come with me!" Hence the story".

Mike Bowyer: "That's as good a reason as any!".

CHAPTER EIGHT

OPERATIONS ON MOSQUITO NIGHT FIGHTERS.
Speaker - Group Captain John Cunningham

Charles Masefield in the Chair:
"Ladies and Gentlemen, as we enter the third and the last session I would like to thank Tony Saint for Chairing the afternoon session of the Programme.

So far today we have heard about the inception of the aircraft, the design, the production, the test flying and the evolution of the various marks. But of course all of that work was aimed at one thing, and that was producing a product that could go to war. This last session is about actually operating the aircraft, to launch into that, who better than undoubtedly one of the outstanding operational pilots, one of the great and the most renowned Mosquito operators - John Cunningham".

John Cunningham took the podium.
"Well thank you Charles, and good afternoon ladies and gentlemen. Operations on the Mosquito night-fighters started at the end of December 1941, when Wing Commander Gordon Slade was given Command of 157 Squadron. Gordon Slade was a Boscombe Down pilot, mainly involved in flying the Mosquito prototype, and before taking Command of 157. He spent some time learning the trade of night-fighting by flying Beaufighters in my Squadron, which was then number 604 and based at Middle Wallop, which was almost next door to Boscombe.

I feel I should briefly cover the rather curious way that night-fighters and night-fighting developed. Fighter Command came into being in 1936 and it was then that 604 Squadron and some other RAF Squadrons were designated as day and night fighters. All the fighter squadrons at that time flew single engined biplanes and the day and night-fighter Squadrons were equipped with the Hawker Demon two seater. The Demon was different to the Hart and all the other Hawker biplanes in that it had a long exhaust pipe from the Rolls Royce Kestrel engine to carry the exhaust away behind the cockpit and so enable the pilot to see ahead at night and not be blinded by the exhaust flames from the usual stub exhausts.

During 1936, 1937 and 1938 very little night flying took place and only occasionally there would be an exercise with searchlights endeavouring to illuminate a target aircraft. I myself never saw or made a practice attack on any aircraft at night during this time. In Autumn 1938 we were mobilized when Germany moved into Czechoslovakia, and it was realized by the Air Ministry that biplane fighters had no chance against the Messerschmitt 109's, already in use in the German Air Force. So a hurried re-equipment of the day and night-fighter Squadrons to Blenheims took place at the end of 1938.

The Blenheim night-fighter had four .303" guns fitted in a tray beneath the fuselage firing forward and one .303" gun in the turret for the Air Gunner - but the Blenheim as a night fighter was completely useless as it had nothing such as radar to help one find and close in on a target. Fortunately there was virtually no enemy activity at night in the winter of 1939 and

Spring of 1940, and Blenheims were used mainly for convoy escort duties by day.

The night-fighter Blenheim squadrons suffered considerable losses at night due to general unfamiliarity by pilots with instrument flying. They flew in blackout conditions with sluggish artificial horizons (particularly just after take-off) with no homing aids and had to operate in low cloud and poor visibility, and as a result, sometimes flew into the nearest piece of high ground.

It was not until the end of September 1940 that the Bristol Beaufighter appeared in the squadron. It was fitted with four 20 millimetre cannons firing forward under the pilots feet, and a radar set that at long last gave the night-fighter squadrons some hope of intercepting the rapidly increasing night bomber raids over England.

It was almost exactly 50 years ago - to be exact, on November 20th 1940, that I was fortunate to shoot down the first German bomber at night over England by means of radar. To learn how to use the radar and make good use of the Beaufighter, took some time, and it was not until April 1941 that the Beaufighters were really beginning to shoot down reasonable numbers of bombers.

The performance of the Beaufighter was only just adequate to deal with Heinkel lll's, Junkers 88's and Dornier 17's, and it was clear that there was no margin in speed to deal with higher speed bombers whenever they were introduced.

It was in May 1941 that the first Mosquito fighter prototype was flown, and I was able to fly it at Hatfield at the beginning of July 1941. I had already flown the prototype Mosquito W4050 in early February 1941, before it went to Boscombe Down, and it was clear to me that when the Mosquito was fitted with radar it would be a splendid replacement for the Beaufighter.

I continued with the Beaufighter in 604 Squadron until the end of July 1942, and after a six month break, I returned to operations as the C.O. of 85 Squadron in February 1943 at Hunsdon near Ware: the squadron was equipped with Mosquito II which used Mk.V radar

Fig.51: The classic Mosquito night-fighter. DD607 showing the early Airborne Interception (A.I.) radar, including the 'Arrowhead' aerials on the nose.

Fig.52: DD737, a NF.Mk.II in night fighter finish. Note the A.I. radar receiver aerials that pass right through the wingtips. (Photo: BAe)

very similar to the Mk.IV equipment fitted in the early Beaufighters. Both these types of radar used external aerials with a 'arrowhead' transmitter aerial on the nose (Fig.51) and receiver aerials on the wings near to the wing tips (Fig.52).

In early 1943, Junkers 88's and Dornier 217's were the main targets, and being faster than the Heinkel III, the night-fighter had less time to make his interception and catch the bomber between the East Coast and London. We also needed longer radar range than we had with our Mk.V radar, and a much better Mosquito night-fighter - the Mk.XII was produced and re-equipped my squadron in March 1943.

Fig.53: From a negative that had suffered the ravages of time comes this picture of DZ659 fitted with the SCR729 radar in the Universal nose. (Photo: BAe)

The new radar was the Mk.VIII, it was housed in a shapely nose-cone (Fig.53) and it was the first 10 centimetre wavelength radar, which did away with all external aerials and used a powerful transmitter with a parabolic reflector housed in the nose cone. It still had its four 20 millimetre cannons firing through your feet of course, but it dispensed with the four machine guns that used to be in the nose of the Mosquito II.

Also in March 1943 my Squadron received 5 Mosquito XV's which had increased wingspan, and an up-rated high altitude Merlin 77, which enabled them to be flown and use their radar at heights above 40,000ft (Fig.54). The four cannon were dispensed with, the four machine guns moving to a pod under the fuselage and it had a bomber type windscreen, all with the object of making it a much lighter and more powerful Mosquito (Fig.55). It really did have a remarkable climb and ceiling. Their expected target was the Junkers 86P high altitude reconnaissance aircraft - which had been flown over England without being intercepted in daylight in the Autumn 1942, but it never materialized at night so this very remarkable Mosquito was never put to good use.

Fig.54:MP469, the prototype F.Mk.XV, photographed at Hatfield on 16 September 1942 following rapid conversion from prototype high altitude bomber to high altitude fighter, with extended wing-tips and four blade propellers. (Photo: BAe)

It was in April 1943 that Focke-Wulf 190's were first used at night, mainly to attack London, and to counter these fast raids my Squadron was moved to West Malling near Maidstone. To our great joy and satisfaction we found that using max continuous power from the Merlin throughout the whole climb - from take-off to interception, and with skilful use of the radar by one's Radar Operator - it was just possible to intercept and close in, identify, and then shoot down a Focke-Wulf 190 carrying a bomb. It was really quite remarkable how the Merlin stood up to such harsh treatment.

By the next month, June 1943, the Messerschmitt 410 appeared over Britain, and with performance very similar to the Mosquito, called for all that the Mosquito could produce in performance to close in and destroy it. In October 1943 the Junkers 188 appeared in operation, and was one of the first German bombers to have a tail-warning radar that made the night-fighter's task more difficult. The German bomber force also began to use Window -

Fig.55:MP469 undergoes engine runs. By now fitted with the Mk.VII radar, so that the four .303"
machines guns had to be relocated into an external under-belly pack. (Photo: BAe)

that was the name given to metal strips that could be dropped in large quantities to confuse
both the ground and airborne radar by illuminating the radar tube and obscuring the radar
return from aircraft in the Window area.

By February 1944 my Squadron was re-equipped with the Mosquito XVII. It had a
change of shape in the nose to house the much improved Mk.10 radar which, with a skilled
radar Operator, could see through Window much better than the earlier Mk.8 radar.

By April 1944 the bomber attacks against London ceased. But in June, the V-1
appeared on the scene and the Mosquito played a major part at night in intercepting and
shooting them down in the area between the Coastal Anti-Aircraft gun belt - where the guns
had freedom to fire at anything - and the London Barrage Balloons.

Until the allied landings in Normandy took place in June 1944 radar-equipped night-
fighters were not allowed to fly over occupied or enemy territory- to make sure that the radar
we used did not fall into enemy hands. But, from June onwards, radar equipped night-
fighters were allowed to fly into Germany and had very many successful sorties.

Having spoken about some of the Mosquito night-fighter activities, I will now briefly
show how the final stages of a night interception took place.

Once radar contact had been made - ideally at some two to three miles range, one's own radar operator would aim to turn one on to a heading that would bring you on to the target's heading and usually slightly below its height. Your operator would call out the range, and you would adjust your speed so that you would close to a range of about 1,000ft. behind your target at the same speed, and about 100-200ft. below it. From that point you might, on a dark night, see a flicker of exhaust flames, for the minimum range that your radar could work to was about 6-800ft.

Having seen the exhausts or an outline of some aircraft, you closed in very slowly right beneath your target so that you could identify what it was. Having satisfied yourself that it was not one of our aircraft you then had to very gradually move back and up to a point immediately behind and about the same level and then, as the target gradually sank down into your gunsight, you fired. We never used tracer in our ammunition because if you did not hit it immediately, you did not advertise your presence and alarm your target.

I clearly remember firing once and seeing no hits - every one in two or three rounds we fired was an explosive shell, which would show if you hit your target and my target or its gunner did not react, and I had to sink down below it and close in further to see it again clearly, and then come up slowly again, and closer, and on the second firing I demolished it!.

Being close behind your target when you hit it, you were liable to fly through bits left in the air - and the only weakness of the Mosquito was that it had its radiators in the leading edge between the engines and the fuselage, and it only needed a piece of perspex or light structure to penetrate it and you lost your coolant, then had to feather your propeller.

Another hazard is well illustrated in (Fig.56) which shows what happened to one of my Squadron's Mosquitoes when it was close in and covered in burning fuel from its target. You will see the cockpit canopy was completely blackened with soot, and all the fuselage

Fig.56: A 'well done' Mosquito!

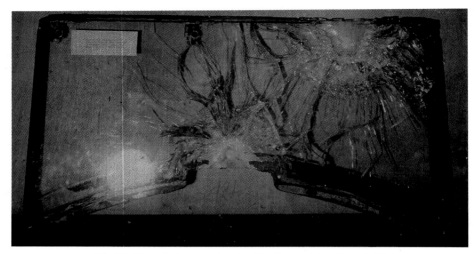

Fig.57: The windscreen showing the damage done by a Ju88

madapolan and wing surface were burnt, and the fabric on the rudder was completely burnt away. Yet this aircraft flew back and landed safely at West Malling.

Finally, there was the hazard of fire from the rear gunner of the target aircraft, and I would not be here today but for the effectiveness of the bullet-proof windscreen (Fig.57) in deflecting two very well aimed shots, from a Junkers 188 that I had just identified from beneath, and just as I was slowly going up to get in position to shoot his gunners saw me and fired on me from above. As my view was spoilt and I had a face showered with small sharp granules from the broken screen, I had to break off the engagement and return to West Malling.

Discussion.
Charles Masefield returned to the podium:
"Well, thank you very much John, now who would like to start the questioning?"

From the floor: "When you closed on a target did you ever use the expression "Bogey, Bogey Waggle your Wings" to identify that it wasn't a friend?

John Cunningham: "No, because we weren't necessarily on the same frequency. I only spoke once, we had a frequency with our ground control station and other aircraft in one's own squadron, but squadrons were working sometimes in each others area and it was quite possible that you would come up on the next squadron's aeroplane in your area, and you could not speak to him and there were mistakes made. Sadly, but generally you had to rely on your own eyesight and identification to make sure you knew what you were shooting at".

From the floor: "We were told John, in heavy aircraft to weave, when you were in enemy territory. It was sometimes difficult to get pilots to weave to anything other than a gentle weave. In your position in following did this weaving have any effect in putting you off?"

John Cunningham: "Only if it was a pretty vigorous weave - a gentle weave, you could follow visually quite happily and choose your moment to shoot that suited the fighter, so a very vigorous weave did put most people off - but not perhaps a very skilled crew".

Maurice Allward: "You mentioned that the Junkers 88 was the first German Bomber to have tail warning radar. Did that give you an advantage as well? - because I understand when we fitted the tail warning radar to the Lancasters, the German kill-rate went up by a factor of six". ·

John Cunningham: "Yes, I think it was possibly a two edged weapon, but it made it very much more difficult for the night-fighter if the aircraft fitted with that tail-warning radar really practically abandoned its task of going and dropping its bomb, and conducted its flight such that it could keep the fighter at a range by slowing down and then turning sharply through 90°, flying on, and turn back through 90°, in one case I spent nearly half-an-hour behind a Messerschmitt 410, that defeated me because it obviously threw away any idea of coming in to London to drop a bomb, and was one of the few Messerschmitt 410's with tail warning radar whose sole object was to hold the fighter from going to someone who had not got a tail-warning radar, if you hung onto it. I was not able to close in - I saw it on one or two occasions, but it used its radar very effectively".

Charles Masefield took the podium: "Thank you very much John for that. At a time when every single airborne interception is controlled by radar it is certainly a privilege to be addressed by the person who made the world's first successful interception and for that we are grateful John".

CHAPTER NINE

DECK LANDING OF THE FIRST TWIN ENGINED AIRCRAFT.

Speaker - Captain Eric Brown

Charles Masefield took the podium:
"Like all good aircraft and certainly true to its multi-role title, the Mosquito did of course go to sea. In fact the very first deck landing of a Mosquito was the very first deck landing of a twin engined aircraft. The person that made that landing was the world's most experienced deck-landing pilot - both in terms of number of deck landings he made, and also in terms of number of types that he had landed on. As far as I know, he may still to this day hold both those records. So, we are certainly privileged to be addressed by Captain Eric Brown".

Captain Eric Brown took the podium.
"Mr Chairman, Ladies and Gentlemen, it is of course a great privilege to be here, and especially to see so many of my RAF colleagues. I want to hasten to reassure them that I am not hand-picked this afternoon to rain on their parade - as a naval officer I feel it is a particular privilege to be in such distinguished company.

Now, you may wonder why the Navy got in to the idea of landing a Mosquito on a carrier. Well it all happened rather suddenly in January 1944. I was then a test pilot in 'C' Squadron in Boscombe Down. I had a call one day from the Admiralty, and the question was very simple - "Do you think you could land a Mosquito on an aircraft carrier?".- Well, with all the brash arrogance of youth I said "yes". When I reconsidered it I wasn't so sure, but I'd burnt my boats by this time, because you must realize that as a form of entertainment, deck landing is probably on a parallel with Russian roulette.

Anyway, when I made this decision I suddenly found myself whisked off to Farnborough, and then, I had to build up some twin-engined time (of which I had very little), and finally on the great day early in March a different than normal Mosquito VI arrived, in that on the rear fuselage a Barracuda-type arrester hook was fitted and the rear fuselage itself was strengthened on either side by reinforced longeron ribs.

The most unusual thing about the aircraft perhaps was the engines themselves. It had two Merlin 25's boosted up to +18lb boost - this was much higher than the normal Merlin was using at that time, and it also had a rather nasty feature, in the sense that it was equipped with two non-feathering four-bladed de Havilland metal propellers - this of course created quite a problem for us.

So this was the aircraft that was to be landed on a carrier. Its serial number was LR359 (Fig.58), and we started to make our preparations.

Now the problems that faced us were these: the speed and weight of the Mosquito was way beyond anything we had dealt with before on an aircraft carrier. One must realize that in 1944 the arrester gear on an aircraft carrier had limitations in that it could only absorb an entry

Fig.58: LR359 - the first ever twin engined aircraft ever to land on a carrier. This Mosquito was a highly modified FB.Mk.VI, and is seen here wearing the Naval Grey/Green scheme and yellow prototype 'P'. (Photo: BAe)

speed of about 65kts, and that for an aircraft of some 10,000lbs weight or so. Here we were talking about an aircraft that in, the official pilots' notes said the approach speed was 125mph, and the weight for the first landings we were going to make was 16,000lbs.

So we had a problem, we had to get the speed down somehow or other, and of course here we would be helped by the carriers speed to create wind over the deck. The other problem was pure dimensions: the flight deck of the carrier we were going to use - *HMS 'Indefatigable'* - had a flight-deck length of 766ft, and a width of 95ft. But that width diminished as you came to the island, which intruded into the main area, leaving only about 80ft. So here we were with an aircraft with a span of 54ft, and we had 80ft space - that was another little one we had to think about.

Another problem was would the undercarriage, which had not been modified, take the vertical velocities which are normally extremely high in deck landing? Or would it collapse under the strain? Also we were of course very nervous about the fact that the whole construction was wood. The decelerations that I have experienced in a deck landing were such that many predicted that the whole thing would be torn in two as the hook caught and the deceleration came on.

Another problem - the crash barrier. Normally when one landed (this was before the days of the angled deck) on a carrier, if you missed the wires or anything went wrong, you went forward in to a crash barrier. This was two steel ropes raised off and strung across the deck with criss-crossed steel wires in it. The idea was that as you went into this in your single-engined aeroplane, your propeller chewed it up and wound it round the engine so that it was all over before it got to you. With the Mosquito you have to admit that the pilot is sitting pretty close to the accident. We had to think again on this one!

Finally there was the matter of single-engined deck landings - was this going to be a possibility? Or, were we even going to be able to go round again if we had an engine problem? Therefore, from early March we set about doing our work up for this.

First thing was to ensure that we could get the aircraft off in the shortest possible space. So in our experiments the technique we finally adopted was to have 25° of flap on, hold the aircraft on the brakes, wind up the Port engine to +4lb boost, the Starboard engine to +2 (the brakes could just hold that) release the brakes, ram on full power and away we go. We found that in the standard atmospheric conditions of atmosphere, pressure and zero wind, we could get the Mosquito VI off at 16,000lbs in 620ft and at 20,000lbs in 820ft - which was quite a performance really.

We then went on to check on the stall and see how that behaved. Contrary to Pat Fillingham's experience with a nice clean ordinary stall, the stall of the Mosquito with power on was quite something else, and we started doing the stalls from zero boost with increments +2, +4 (+4 was the maximum we went to). When it stalled at these power settings the stick cracked hard over in the cockpit to the left with such violence that you could not hold it and the aircraft dropped its wing violently to over the vertical. So it was quite clear that if we got low and slow on the approach it was going to be a fatality.

However, we did find that we could hold the aircraft at +4lbs boost and get the speed down to something we felt would be less than a hundred miles an hour. So the approach, we determined, would have to be made at this boost, literally hanging on the props the whole way in, finally cutting the engines three feet above the deck and letting it just fall on. That way we would probably arrive without any risk of a wing drop and also probably we would not impose too heavy loads on the undercarriage.

So, we had our approach weighed up, now it was a question of single-engine approaches. With the non-feathering propellers we found we could not even go round again, far less make a single-engined approach. We could not really go below 500ft, because the aircraft could not be held at any speed below 170mph with one propeller wind-milling and the other actually operating at full boost. You ran out of rudder, so you never could get up to full boost, since you could not hold it anyway. Single-engine landings were absolutely out and so was going round again because we don't operate above 500ft in deck landings - as you can appreciate.

So, we went on to the first check of the landing into the wires and took the aircraft up to Arbroath, where there are a set of arrestor wires laid out on the runway, and conducted a number of run-ins there, really to prove the installation - that is the hook installation - there were no great problems involved at all.

We then went on to an airfield just below Arbroath called East Haven, which was the Deck Landing Control Officers school where the dreaded Batsman would stand there on an aircraft carrier with his paddles - which I could never relate to - and tell you what to do, I don't know how the hell they know what you're doing - but there we are! They only compounded the problem as far as I was concerned. But, their Lordships dictated we had to have a Batsman and so the Commanding Officer of the Batsman's School, no more, no less, was elected.

He found out, well I found out, that I couldn't see him at all in the normal position as I approached, because the port engine was between him and me. So I informed him of this, but I did not quite expect the ballet performance we got on the actual landing.

Now to the first landing, this occurred on the 25th of March. So you see we hadn't really had much time between getting the aircraft early in March to making the actual first landing.

The aircraft, strangely enough, behaved extremely well on the approach and this photograph , (Fig.59) is just at the point where I cut the throttles. I caught the second wire, there are about 8-10 wires on HMS Indefatigable, and the actual touch-down speed was, believe it or not 78mph. When you consider as I said that the RAF pilots' notes say 125mph, that is quite a reduction. But, at that stage I am just cutting from plus 4lbs boost on each engine,which is held right to the last moment. That was made at 16,000lbs and there was 40kt of speed over the deck (a ship could do about 30kts and we had 10kts of natural wind). Then we carried on the landings mounting up the weight.

All went well until the eighth landing which was at the weight of 18,000lbs, and when at touch-down I felt the deceleration start, which is normal when you catch a wire, then suddenly it stopped, and the aircraft began to move forward again. Well, I had to make a lightning assessment - one of two things could have happened: either the hook had broken in which case we had to go on - incidentally there was no crash barrier of course because we

Fig.59:Captain Eric Brown lands LR359 on *HMS Indefatigable* on 25 March 1944. Clearly shown here is the arrestor hook that caught the 2nd wire and the fact that the Mosquito's starboard undercarriage leg is on the carriers deck centreline.

hadn't developed a specialised crash barrier - I am going to come to that later. We just hadn't had time to develop an adequate crash barrier, so I could take off again if the hook had actually broken. If the wire had broken however, which was quite possible with these higher weights, which were unusual on carriers. Then if I opened up again too early I might cause another disaster and pull the hook out, because I had to wait to give it sufficient time to get to at least one more wire. We did get to this position, when I realized that something had gone wrong that was not going to arrest us. So I had to give it the full-gun, irrespective of the swing and the torque caused, fortunately the torque in the Mosquito takes you to port,and of course by this time we were up and near the Island, and so I just let it swing straight over the side - all was well.

What actually happened was to the claw of the arrester hook. The claw is held on to the frame of the hook by a couple of bolts, and the forward bolt had sheared, therefore allowing the claw to rotate and the wire was thrown out clear of the claw. Of course the hook also snapped back up into position. There was no question of stopping so we had to go on.

The aircraft was sent back to Hatfield, who very rapidly modified it, and put a strengthened bolt in and also made sure that the snap gear would not allow the hook to lock up if such an incident actually happened again. Also, we fitted a tail wheel lock during this period - but that really didn't make any odds at all.

Now with the take-off technique, of course, we could not line the aircraft on the central line of the flight deck because of the Island, so we had to put the starboard wheel on the centre line, and take it from there. But it was much easier than on land to control the swing, because you already had the wind speed, and the ship's natural speed to give you some control over the rudder.

In the second series of landings I introduced a second pilot with me into the business. He flew aboard with me for the first time and I demonstrated how it was done, and we worked the weights up 16,000, 18,000 up to 20,000lbs - that was the max weight we landed at!

I then went on alone to do take-offs up to 21,500lb which necessitated carrying bombs aboard, and of course with that strange sense of humour the Admiralty had, the bombs were live! I was told to drop them, but they didn't say drop them well away from the carrier; I was meant to know that myself! So I made a wide circuit and dropped these live, they went off with a very nice bang, and we were able to land back on at about 20,000lb. So all told the whole thing was a very successful exercise.

Now really there is a bit of a tale, or should I say a postscript to this whole thing, because in September 1944 at Farnborough there arrived a Mosquito IV, with an arrester hook on it, and it had the serial number DZ537/G. Those of you who were in the war involved in testing knew that that oblique stroke 'G' was to indicate a top secret aircraft. All the original jets at Farnborough had this oblique stroke 'G' on them and here it was on this ordinary Mosquito (apart from the fact that it had a hook on it). I was told that I was to run it into the wires at Farnborough to a very much reduced retardation value compared to that used for our trials type of aircraft. Nobody would tell me what it was all about - this 'G' had really closed mouths - not a squeak until about three weeks later I was suddenly despatched up to RAF Beccles near Ipswich and told I had to teach 618 Squadron to deck land. Nobody said why 618 had been chosen for this unfortunate fate. But there we are!

Anyway, when I got there I found in the hangar one Doctor Barnes Wallis walking around. The Mosquito bomb doors were open and there was this spherical type of bomb that was used in the Dam-Busters Raid fitted to the aircraft. I found out that what was on was a thing called 'Operation Highball', which was going to be a raid by Mosquitoes on capital ships in the harbour in Japan.

The idea was it was going to be a sort of Jimmy Doolittle type of raid, where they were going to take-off from a carrier and make their attack and then the difficult part came after that - they were going to have to get back on to the carrier. In fact 27 Mosquitoes were loaded aboard the escort carrier 'Striker', which left the Clyde on 30 October 1944, and went out on its way to Australia. The operation never took place for the simple reason the War ended before the whole thing was set up. But nevertheless that was what was intended.

Very finally of course, the Navy (in the light of the success of these trials) decided to order 50 production Sea Mosquito TR33's very similar to the Mk.VI (Figs.60 & 61). From the 14th aircraft onwards they were to have folding wings (Fig.62) and long-stroke oleos for the heavy landings that were to be anticipated on the carrier deck. They were also to have the capability of carrying an 18 inch torpedo plus two 250lb bombs (Figs..63, 64 & 65).

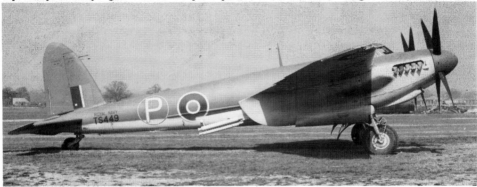

Figs. 60 & 61: Two views of TS449, one of a pair of prototype TR/TF.Mk.33 Mosquitoes used for service trials. This Leavesden-built machine had four-bladed propellers, Rocket Assisted Take-Off Gear (RATOG) fitted behind the wing and an arrestor hook (Photos: BAe)

Fig.62: A close-up of the wing folding hinges, immediately outboard of the flaps, showing the locking pins and release mechanism, with the locking pin release lever in the fully extended position as fitted to the Sea Mosquito. (Photo:BAe)

Fig.63: LR387, the second prototype TR.Mk.33 with the wings folded. (Photo:BAe)

Figs. 64 & 65 - Two further photographs of what is thought to be LR387, a TR.Mk.33 converted from a FB.Mk.VI in 1945. The 18 inch torpedo and its supports and the ASH radar is clearly shown in this close up. (Photos: BAe)

Now these Sea Mosquitoes were in fact built but little used on a carrier deck, for a reason that will be explained - Incidentally there was a determination to use them originally on a carrier deck in the Japanese war, because I did tests with rocket assisted take-off gear fitted to the Mk.33, to make sure they could get off at full load in the hot climate to be experienced in the Far East. These tests were totally successful, so fundamentally there was no reason why it shouldn't be operated, but basically the reason was this: the Hornet. The beautiful Sea Hornet to my mind was the most beautiful aircraft I have ever flown in my life, for pure unadulterated joy of handling. One could feel a sort of *joie de vivre* in this aircraft. It was a single seat hot-rod Mosquito, and it is a delight to be in something that is totally over-powered of course.

So there we are, but the reason the Admiralty decided in favour of the Hornet was they felt if the Navy was going to be in introduced to twin engined flying it should have the latest model with a lot of the problems removed from the Mosquito.

The question of swing was removed by the handed propellers in this aircraft and there was also a much better chance one could certainly do an over-shoot, and go round again in the Hornet on one engine.

What did we do about a specialised twin crash barrier?. Fundamentally it was just two strands of wire - one strand of wire to catch the undercarriage legs. As it did, the aircraft came up, and there was a high strand that caught the tail to stop the aircraft flipping over on its back. It was highly successful, but was not used very much, for the Hornet proved very easy to use on deck.

Fig.66: The cockpit layout of the TR.Mk.37 Sea Mosquito. (Photo: BAe)

Fig.67: VT724, a TR.Mk.37 showing the oleo-pneumatic undercarriage installed for carrier deck landings. (Photo:BAe)

So that was how it was allstarted. A very happy story about the Mosquito, it made itself a bit of history and I have the greatest possible affection for the aircraft and its successor. Thank you.

Discussion.

Mr Charles Masefield took the podium:

"Well if anyone can think of a more exciting way of earning a living than doing those early deck landings I'd like to hear about it. Now could we have some questions?"

Mike Ramsden: "Could we hear what the Mosquito was like to fly? - I know that this is a very general question, but was it what we would call to-day a Pilot Friendly' aeroplane and what did you have to particularly watch for?"

Eric Brown: "It was a pilot's aeroplane - in fact I never flew a de Havilland product that was not a pilot's aeroplane. The Mosquito was a delightful aircraft to fly from my point of view. Somebody asked what it was like to dog-fight. I was in a naval unit once that did a check on this type of capability. The aircraft was not capable of taking on a average contemporary single-seat fighter in a dog-fight. One had to be careful that you did not pull it round too hard at full power, for as I said if it stalled under power you had a very nasty flick-out indeed. But it could certainly see off any twin-engined fighter in the world at that time. The Hornet on the other hand could see off any twin and a good number of singles as well - a great aeroplane for the pilot".

From the floor: May I ask if you ever had any experience of landing a Corsair under full load?"

Eric Brown: "Yes. Not a happy experience! The Corsair was a very difficult aircraft to deck-land, for two very fundamental reasons. One, it had an appalling view - it had a very long nose and a very strange cockpit. If you were on a long flight and got tired you could go for a walk around the stick!. I found out later that this happened because the Chief Test pilot of Chance-Vought was six feet four inches tall!. I flew the aircraft most of the time half on my back so that I could reach the rudder pedals. This is not conducive to good deck landings. Quite apart from that it had a very nasty torque stall. It had a very large, powerful engine and very large propeller. If you got slow on the approach, away it went and would invert itself: we lost a lot of pilots that way.

From the floor. "I think here is the opportunity to hear briefly the utter drama of landing an aircraft on a carrier in a fairly large sea with low visibility. Could you please take us through the excitement?"

Eric Brown replied: "Well, landing on an aircraft carrier is never easy - one never gets used to it! It always looks like a stamp floating in a large bathtub. You may have been away on combat or a very long exercise . At the end of the day you have perhaps even a tougher proposition facing you - you have to get home. If the weather is not of the best, you have two problems - the ship is probably moving a considerable amount. The worst case I have ever experienced was landing on an escort carrier in the north Atlantic. I had to get down, for it was just before dusk and the stern was moving 60ft; that is +/- 30ft. The ship was rolling to the order of 30° either side. This is of course an utterly extreme example and in that circumstance you have to try to hit the fulcrum point of the ship, where movement is at the minumum.

Besides pitch and roll the worse thing is heave, where the whole ship is moving up and down. It is because of heave that strengthened undercarriages were needed. Your only hope in bad visibility was to see and follow the wake of the ship, which occurred long before the hull appeared out of the gloom - that's how it is".

Charles Masefield took the podium:

"How do you follow that? I think that is a good point to stop. Thank you very much Eric and, for another occasion I do happen to know that some bright spark in either the Air Ministry or the War Office decided that hooks were a thing of the past and with the introduction of either the Vampire or maybe it was the Venom someone had the bright idea to suggest landing these on a rubber mattress with the wheels up. Guess who received the telephone call to come and prove if it was possible or not? Eric Brown was later seen landing wheels up at either Boscombe or Farnborough onto rubber mattresses. I do not know how much he enjoyed it, but it never seemed to catch on with the many in the Navy. Thank you very much Eric".

CHAPTER TEN

OPERATIONS OF 617 SQUADRON.
Speaker - Jim Shortland

Charles Masefield took the podium:
"Now of course the Mosquito didn't take long to find its way into service with 617 'The Dam-Busters' Squadron as a pathfinder and Jim Shortland is now going to tell us about pathfinder operations and precision bombing with 617 Squadron".

Jim Shortland took the podium.
"Good evening Ladies and Gentlemen. Can I also say what a privilege it is to be here this evening in such distinguished company.

Two things occurred to me this afternoon that I had not really thought of before: the first one is, I appear to be the youngest person to stand here today - so perhaps those of you that are older than me will say he's too young to know what he's talking about' - well if you

Fig.68: A poor quality, but very impressive photograph of a 4,000lb thin-skinned store just after release. (Photo: BAe)

give me perhaps half an hour then I may prove one or two things wrong ; secondly, I thought they ought to change the name over the entrance to BAe to perhaps MFI - being furniture manufacturers in the second World War and call themselves 'Mosquito Fighters Indestructible'.

I do have a claim on de Havilland aircraft for, during my National Service, I was an engine fitter and actually worked on NF.10's, and T.11's at RAF Shawbury. My first ever flight was after having completed an intermediate service on a Vampire NF.10 aircraft with its wooden surround in which you sat in - at 20,000 ft this caused me some concern! - and the fact that I had just serviced the aircraft! So I do have some connection (although many years' ago) with de Havilland aircraft.

When I was asked to come down from 'Bomber County'- we live in Lincolnshire, about 20 miles south of Lincoln, and my specialist subject is 617's Squadron's operational history from 1943 to 1945. I thought it would be rather nice to tell those of you who weren't aware of the fact that 617 Squadron used Mosquitoes, about the way in which they operated, and to give you some idea of what they did at Woodhall Spa. Firstly, I'll give you a brief introduction to the Squadron's history - why and where they were formed, then go in to the use of Mosquitoes by 617 Squadron and 627 Squadron - who were also based at Woodhall Spa during 1944-45.

Briefly the Squadron's crest shows three forked lightning bolts over a breached dam with the motto *'Apres moi, le deluge'* which translated means, 'After me the floods'. The Squadron was formed in March 1943 at RAF Scampton, an airfield just to the north of Lincoln where they shared the base with 57 Squadron. They were there until September 1943 and then moved down the road to a pre-war base, RAF Coningsby, whilst 57 Squadron moved from Scampton to a new base at East Kirkby.

617 Squadron weren't very long at Coningsby; they were there in late August 1943 but left in earlyJanuary 1944 and moved to a relatively small airfield north of Coningsby called Woodhall Spa.

One cannot talk about 617 Squadron in any way shape or form without a special mention of the late Dr. Barnes Wallis. Barnes Wallis designed three of the weapons that the Squadron used during the second World War, one of which was the bouncing-bomb or mine. He had this idea that if he was able to reduce the Germans' water supply, he would be able to create enormous problems in the manufacture of steel, which needed large amounts of hydro-electric power for its production. If he could bounce a mine over the water and and then roll it down the front of the Dam, it would explode with pistol fuses and therefore burst the Dam. This was Barnes Wallis's idea!

The whole thing was put in to operation by Sir Ralph Cochrane, AOC of 5 Group, and Wing Commander Guy Gibson was given a very difficult task of forming the Squadron and carrying out this rather difficult operation. They did carry out the operation successfully using specially modified Lancasters - two of the five Dams attacked were breached. So, that briefly puts you in perspective that the Squadron was formed as a specialized bombing unit, and that gives you some idea of what these young lads did.

19 aircraft went on the 'Dams' raid and 53 aircrew were lost on that night. Very soon afterwards Gibson left and went on a tour of the States, and Squadron Leader George Holden took over the Squadron on September 1943, but he was lost on a raid to the Dortmund-Ems

canal.

The Squadron was taken over then temporarily by Micky Martin, and because he was only a Flight Lieutenant, Cochrane would not allow him to be promoted to Wing Commander and take charge of the Squadron, so Leonard Cheshire was appointed as Commanding Officer. He in fact had just completed a tour with a Halifax Squadron in Yorkshire and had been promoted to Group Captain, but he dropped a rank to Wing Commander to take charge of 617. The squadron was still very much a 'special' unit, manned mainly by volunteer veteran crews that specialised in ultra low-level operations - a form of flying that was very much in line with Cheshire's preferences.

He realized from his previous experience that one of the problems during the early part of the Second World War was actually finding and marking the targets. He did actually go down to a base, RAF Sculthorpe in Norfolk, where he tried a Mosquito in December 1943 - because I am sure he had the intention of using a Mosquito at later dates. So he tried a Mosquito out but it wasn't until around March 1944 that he went to Coleby Grange, (which is an airfield about 10 miles north of where we live in Sleaford) to again try out a Mosquito, this time a Mk.XII belonging to 307 (Polish) Squadron for half an hour.

When I spoke to Leonard Cheshire, I asked him why had he not put in the log book the name of the Mosquito pilot who he first flew with at Colby Grange, and he said,"Have you tried spelling some of these difficult Polish surnames?" So Leonard, in his log book, didn't mention the pilots name, but obviously he was aware of it, and fairly soon afterwards he took delivery of a Mosquito.

This was not 617 Squadron's first experience of the Mosquito, for on 15 September

Fig.69:A Mosquito and its crew at Woodhall Spa in 1944. Right is the pilot Flt Lt Gerry Fawke DSO, DFC with his navigator F/O Tom Bennett DFM. (Photo: Tom Bennett)

Above - Fig.70: The same aircraft is pushed back into its hangar. Below - Fig.71: A close up of the nose of this machine, showing sixteen sorties symbols, the artwork and name *'The Artistocrat'* (Photos: Tom Bennett)

1943 three crews and their aircraft were detached from 418 (City of Edmonton) Squadron RCAF to support 617 on a special raid against the Dortmund-Ems Canal, the Mosquitoes attacking enemy defences in the area.

Cheshire developed (with the help of people like David Shannon, Gerry Fawke, Terry Kearns and Micky Martin) a technique of using a Lancaster as a 'Type of dive-bomber'. The idea was that he would put these spot-fires on to illuminated targets, that would have been illuminated by a pathfinder force using H2S Radar. So that they could actually drop sky markers in the target area, Cheshire would go down at fairly low level with a Lancaster and drop his spot-fires. Obviously with an aircraft of this size, and with a crew of six or more people, he realized that this was a particularly dangerous operation. But he actually went in at very low level to accurately mark the Gnôme-Rhône aero-engine works at Limoges in France which resulted in the complete destruction of the factory with no casualties amongst the local French civilians.

Fig.72: The night of 25/26 March 1944, and the target is the aero engine factory at Lyons. This picture shows the ground from 10,700ft and demonstrates just how good the target illuminating flares were. (Photo: Jim Shortland Collection)

So from this point on, all of these raids were Mosquito marked and identified. The first actual Mosquito operation occurred on 5 April 1944 when Cheshire flying ML976 'N' marked a target at Toulouse. Thereafter several crews flew other Mosquitoes to mark targets for the Squadron's Lancasters.

One of the targets that Leonard claims to be his most rewarding (if that is the word to use) and one that was mentioned in his citation when he was awarded his VC, was the bombing operation on Munich. To enable the Mosquitoes to reach Munich (they could not fly direct from Woodhall Spa) they went down to RAF Manston and re-fuelled, and from there went direct to Munich then returned back to Manston to re-fuel. Approaching the airfield with almost dry fuel tanks, Cheshire nearly fell victim to a marauding German intruder.

On 13 April 1944 another Mosquito squadron moved into Woodhall Spa. This was 627 Squadron, officially detached from 8 Group to 5 Group and was to remain there until the end of the war.

As you may know, 8 Group's 'Pathfinder Force' used numerous electronic equipment to aid target marking from high altitude - 627 preferred to use the Mk.I eyeball at low level. Much practice on the ranges at Wainfleet Sands revealed that the best technique was to dive from 3,000ft and release the stores at 1,000ft. In combat conditions this was very much at the mercy of weather conditions, for the aircrew had to identify the target and make a shallow dive ending in a low-level run before the target markers could be released from as little as 100ft.

627 were the sole Mosquito squadron in 5 Group and they operated primarily as a marker unit for the many Lancaster attacks mounted by the Group against Germany. Many of these Lancaster raids used another weapon specially designed by Barnes Wallis - a 12,000lb 'Tallboy' Bomb.

The Tallboy weapons were manufactured at the English Steel Corporation (ESC) in Sheffield, and had a very thick molybdenum steel nose, filled with 'Torpex' and had a Shorts of Belfast-manufactured tail cone. For those of you who are technically minded they were cast in special sand mouldings, housed in the same area where before the war ESC used to cast church bells. They were the only people in the U.K who could manufacture these nose cones. On the production type versions the tail fins were inclined at 5 degrees to the centre line, so soon after the bomb left the aircraft it adopted a nose down attitude, the wind speed through the fins caused it to rotate. From an altitude in excess of 23,000ft it would hit the ground supersonically, the tailcone would break off and themain bullet section of the bomb would actually enter the ground in soft earth up to 90ft. This weapon eventually became known on the Squadrons as the 'Earthquake Bomb'.

A contract was placed with the Millwaukee Steel Corporation in the States that produced some interesting differences. The British version was cast, then turned very accurately on a centre-lathe, being skimmed to within +/- 0.002". The American versions were simply rough cast and cleaned up with a disc grinder. Therefore this affected the gyroscopic action and they did not have the same degree of accuracy as the U.K made ones. The nose cone was all metal, and the tail cone really was like a dart flight, that actually guided the whole thing down to the ground.

The first time these were used was on the Saumur railway tunnel in central France. The

Germans were down in Northern Italy, expecting our second front to be there, but they were wrong - we were up in Normandy. The result was that they moved large concentrations of railway-carried Panzer divisions through the railway tunnel at Saumur. It went through the tunnel before the river Loire, and then over the river on a bridge.

It was marked on the night of the 8th of June by Leonard Cheshire and Gerry Fawke and then attacked. It is interesting to note, particularly for me as an alleged historian, that on that night Terry Kearns no less, flew with Squadron Leader Richardson as the bomb aimer Squadron Leader Richardson was an ex-Boscombe Down specialist, who was the instructor of the the stabilizing automatic bomb-sight (SABS) that the Squadron used.

They were the only Squadron to operate using the sight. This was a gyroscopic bomb-sight, and certainly without going into too much technical detail about the sight, it was gyroscopically driven with vertical and horizontal gyros inside it. It was extremely difficult for the pilots to fly with, because they had to lock on to the target some 10 miles before they got there and fly dead level, no ducking and weaving, and during the approach the navigator made several calculations, radioed the information through to the bomb-aimer, who set the various dials and readings.

Although all of the markers were dropped very close to the target, not all of the bombs fell so accurately. One fell , or dare I say dropped off, and fell inert, the result being that it caused a very large hole but didn't go off, in a street the French now call *Route de la Torpedo*.

As I mentioned earlier, 83 Squadron with their H2S marked the Saumur tunnel with sky markers, and they then went on to mark the bridge that went over the river Loire, This was bombed by two Lancasters of 617 Squadron where they had immense success - using the Mosquito method of marking. They then went on to bomb the E-Boat shelters in Boulogne, because they were sending out the surface torpedo carrying German ships, small boats, and attacking our supply vessels in the Channel, so the Squadron went to the E-Boat pens at Boulogne, they also went to the E-boat shelters in Le Havre.

As many of the raids were in occupied Europe, concern was expressed that the civilian population should be affected as little as possible. The Mosquitoes marking technique could minimise any danger to the local populace by very accurately marking both ends of the target under attack so that the Lancasters following along behind could drop their bomb load between the two sets of markers. One such example was a small factory that had been previously attacked by the USAAF in daylight from high level that was completely undamaged. 627 were called in and marked the target with ease, although a small problem did occur when the first batch of markers fell through the glass roof of the factory and became almost invisible!.

617 Squadron and its Mosquitoes also attacked a number of V-1, V-2 and V-3 sites. It also must be remembered that the Germans were working on the A-4 (V-2), but they got as far as the A-5, and the A-9 in the design stage. The A-9 and 10 was the two stage V-2, which would probably go to America. The A-5 was a winged version, designed to be fired from Wizerns, and no doubt reaching the Northern part of England. The Germans had been well aware that the Allies would target these structures, so took defensive measures to make sure that they were as difficult as possible to destroy. They actually built the roof 21ft thick, at Watten, building the roof on the ground first, then jacked the whole thing up, removed the

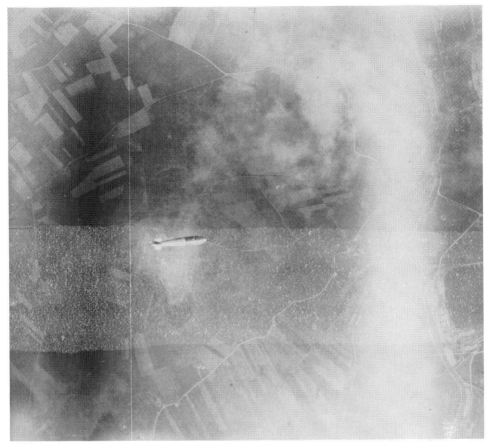

Fig. 73: A 12,000lb 'Tallboy' soon after release from a 617 Squadron Lancaster on 19 June 1944, the target being the V2 site at Watten in northern France. (Photo: Jim SHortland Collection)

went on until the correct height was reached.

The importance of these precision raids cannot be under-estimated - having picked up the target 10 miles away and locked on with automatic release, the Tallboy went down, and it was a fairly high degree of success, in fact so successful were the American and British raids on Watten, that the Germans changed its use from V2 firing to a liquid oxygen plant, for another V-2 site down the road at Wizerns. When the Squadron marked this it was a daylight raid, the Tallboys had instant impact fuses, they were capable of having delayed action fuses - up to half an hour in fact. But they were impact fuses, and the problem was when the early Lancasters went in and dropped their Tallboys, the huge plumes of chalk dust created problems, so later Lancasters had to go round again and pick up the route 10 miles out and re-commence their bombing run!

Towards the latter part of the war those aircrew who had gained the most experience were used to great effect by 627 which employed them in the role of 'Master Bomber'. They directed the attack of the Main Force via a VHF radio link as they orbitted the target, often at low-level, and would call in for more indicators if required. It was while engaged on one such sortie that 54 Squadron's Base Operations Officer, unofficially taking the role of Master Bomber to direct the attack against Rheydt in the Ruhr valley, met his death while flying Mosquito KB267 during the night of 29/30 September 1944. That officer's name, who had volunteered for the operation in order to relieve the boredom of his desk job, was Wing Commander Guy Gibson VC.

Unfortunately we appear to have ran out of time and there is really still so much more to talk about - the raids on the U-Boat Pens, Shipping and many other targets, but I am forced to call a halt there. Thank you very much".

Charles Masefield returns to the podium:
"Thank you very much Jim. It was nice to hear about the Mosquito, a Hatfield product working hand in glove with the Lancaster, a Woodford product to mark the target and then obliterate it. Of course now we have Hatfield and Woodford working hand in glove on the 146 production. Those down here would say that Hatfield provides the finesse and Woodford provides the brute force and it seems it was always thus".

CHAPTER ELEVEN

HISTORICAL PERSPECTIVE.

Speaker - Mike Ramsden

Charles Masefield took the podium:
"Finally, Mike Ramsden is going to wrap up the proceedings for us by putting all of this in to a historical perspective for the last few minutes, Mike...".

Mike Ramsden takes the podium.
"Well, I think it is customary to say what an act to follow; I think one can say that about every performer today, and I've got the job of following one of the most wonderful days that I have ever spent in listening to an aviation symposium. So it really is for all of us who regarded the Mosquito with awe and respect before we came here. I can say for myself that I regard it with even greater awe and respect now. I can only just give a few fleeting and rather personal impressions of what I've noted down during the day, and then - as we're in injury time already - to sum up the historical perspective.

David Newman spoke about the Ministry and briefing the Ministry on technicalities. Surprisingly during the day, we haven't really had very much of the Government's role; but they were not what Goering called 'nincompoops' obviously, because Government have always been, as they are now, a member of the partnership. That the Mosquito was such a success I think the Ministry could take some of the credit.

A personal comment on the Whirlwind. Somebody said, "Why does it look so like the Mosquito? Why didn't it quite become as successful as the Mosquito? I think it was launched to a specification that was issued for a heavy cannon fighter about a year, or perhaps even more, before the Mosquito - which of course as we know was an unarmed bomber.

Listening to Mr Harvey-Bailey from Rolls Royce ,we heard words with which we who have been brought up in the airframe business are perhaps not quite so current: nitrous oxide injection, epicyclic supercharger, Farman drives and reverse-flow cooling. What a debt the Mosquito owes to Rolls Royce. Charles Masefield I think got it right when he said,'That engine did as much as any aircraft to win the War'.

Mr Harvey-Bailey mentioned hand-fitting, a particular process in the production of a particular model of a particular Mark, and he said that 'Packard didn't like hand-fitting'. That reminded me of a story that I'd heard about the Packard Merlin not being particularly reliable, unlike the British-built equivalent. They kept having crankcase cracking, and when they tracked this down, they found that Packards had been going according to the drawings, whereas the Merlin had been fixed in the foundry by Joe, who was doing the casting - who thought, 'Oh that bit is not quite thick enough - I'll make it a bit thicker'. So the Americans are different, but thank goodness for them.

I was over-awed by the quiet way in which Mr Harvey-Bailey said that within a year or two after the Battle of Britain the Merlin was producing 2,050hp double the horse-power of the Spitfire and the Hurricane in the Battle of Britain.

That end-to-end crank shaft lubrication was fascinating too, because it's another example of lost lessons. He said that Lotus is doing it today, and also for the American Corvette.

The Hornet. Ah, the Hornet! I've learnt so many things today. I didn't know that the 130 Merlin had actually been packaged - I think the words used were, 'especially for de Havilland'.

I think we can assure Pat Fillingham that the Mosquito is a monoplane! And that our memories have really been given a treat today. That story about Mr Bishop doing a real hands-on-chief designer job trying to get his under-carriage down. I liked that one very much indeed!

I didn't know about the icing problem - or the lack of de-icing which the Mosquito had. That could perhaps have been the cause of losses.

I'd like to know whether the audience thinks that plural Mosquitoes, like Tornadoes or other aeroplanes ending in 'o', should be spelt with an 'e' or with an 's': Tornados sounds like an under-done steak or something. Hands up those who think that it should be 'oes' - this is a real Conservative party vote here! Hands up all of those who think it should be 'os' - I think the 'e' has it! As in Concorde!

Listening to John Cunningham who, as Charles Masefield said, was the first man actually to do what is normal today, using radar for interception, was really quite awe-inspiring. What he didn't say, being as modest as he is, was something I know. It was a little throw away which some of you may not have noticed. He said that he flew the prototype W4050 before it went to Boscombe. Well, has anybody realized what the implication of that is? Because I don't think that any squadron pilot has ever flown a prototype aircraft before Boscombe has flown it. I don't think that has ever happened since or before, and of course it must have been due to a very special combination of circumstances. I think John had been a test pilot here and I think that the Chief of the Air Staff, Lord Portal, was quite close to Sir Geoffrey de Havilland. I don't know, but that was a piece of typical John modesty.

One of the most awesome presentations of the day I thought, was by Captain Eric Brown. We were listening to someone who has made more deck-landings than any other man, and he himself described deck-landings as, let's see if I can remember what he said,"...*as a form of entertainment deck landing is rather like a form of Russian roulette*". So there you have it!.

It reminded me of what Mr Bishop had said to me when I interviewed him. Over lunch he talked about the Mosquito, and about the most difficult design job he had ever done, and he said, "I gave it to Tamblin to do". And it was the Sea Mosquito's folding wing. He said,"I gave it to Tamblin and he did it and got it right". And it really was the most remarkably difficult job. I found a photograph of it the other day, and I sent it to a friend in Boeing who's got the job of designing the folding wing on the 777. Mr Bishop told me that it was going to be hydraulically powered or automatically powered, until an Admiral said, "*Oh don't worry about that we've got lots of sailors who can do it*". And the photograph shows about eight sailors with an enormous lever, and an incredible hinge device.

Lovely to hear Captain Brown say of the Hornet, "*To my mind this was the most beautiful aircraft I had ever flown in my life*". And that's from a test pilot who I think has flown two or three hundred types of aircraft. "A total delight", he said. That was the Hornet, the offspring or daughter of the aeroplane we have been discussing today. It was nice also to hear him say, when I asked him about the Mosquito and what it was like to fly, *"I have never flown a de Havilland aircraft that wasn't nice to fly"*.

Paradoxical I think that those 'Tallboy' bombs were being cast by a mould made for church bells.

What an aircraft!. What role could it not do? - we've even heard words today like dog fighting and heavy bombing - comparing it with heavy bombers!. We've heard of it as a transport aircraft; we've even heard of it as a carrier borne aircraft which was going to take-off from aircraft carriers and bomb Tokyo.

It really isn't a subjective de Havilland remark to say that it must be one of the most remarkable aircraft of all time. That has been well brought out today, and we have a great vote of thanks to give to the organizers - the Royal Aeronautical Society's Hatfield branch, who've arranged all this, and picked all the speakers.

The Mosquito was above all an aircraft industry achievement, a British industry achievement. A recent book called, 'Britain's Aircraft Industry' I'll mention the name of the author - it's perhaps an abuse of my power as a public speaker at the moment, but I felt so annoyed by it Professor Kenneth Haywood. This book does not actually even mention the Mosquito, yet that aircraft was not only a performer of a great many roles: it was also a great industrial achievement, what we call 'cost effective' today, all the things that we try to achieve in the aircraft we do today. It made a very small demand on material resources and human resources and it was easy to make, easy to repair, and easy easy to fly - all good things. Anyway there we are, the book on the British Aircraft Industry, just recently published, doesn't mention the Mosquito.

To go back in conclusion to Pat Fillingham's lovely talk. When he was in the cinema, a notice came up saying, *'The weather has cleared and will the de Havilland pilots please go back to Hatfield'*. Well let's hope the weather has cleared and that a sign will come up saying that tomorrow we shall actually see the Mosquito".

Mr Charles Masefield took the podium:
"Well thank you very much Mike for that tour de force, which I certainly won't attempt to follow. It only remains for me thank again all the organizers for today, to thank again all the speakers for their magnificent contributions, and especially to thank everyone, this huge audience which has certainly exceeded the expectations for coming along today".

CHAPTER TWELVE

THE SYMPOSIUM DINNER

During the Saturday evening a celebratory dinner was held at British Aerospace, Apart from the more formal speeches, which are reproduced in edited form below, there were a number of interesting or humorous anecdotes told. Because of the highly unofficial nature of these stories it is impossible to check the historical accuracy. Nevertheless, all do make fascinating reading and give an invaluable insight into the lighter side to the goings on. This is a selection of those stories.

The introductory speech was made by Lee Balthazor:
"Ladies and gentlemen, the 50th Anniversary of the first flight of the Mosquito is an appropriate event to formally launch the R E Bishop Memorial Award. Although we have touched on it already today, it is worth recapping for a number of people have joined us tonight.

Actually we were trying to work out just how many 'first flights' there were in the Mosquito - perhaps there is someone in the audience that could tell us just how many different marks of Mosquito did fly - we'll come to that in the anecdotes!.

The R E Bishop Memorial Award, organised and sponsored by the Hatfield branch of the Royal Aeronautical Society and sponsored jointly by British Aerospace Hatfield and the Royal Aeronautical Society has two aims. First to provide a fitting memorial to R E Bishop, who was responsible for the innovative design of this remarkable aircraft we have heard about today.

Secondly, the aim that we thought was most appropriate to act as a memorial was to encourage school-children to become interested in aerospace in particular and engineering. It is also designed to foster and promote the idea of teamwork within those youngsters. Therefore what we have done is to start a small pilot scheme locally here in six schools with the intention that small teams in those schools will work together on a particular project and the winning team from each school will then come here to Hatfield for a final, where we will then award the winning team the R E Bishop Memorial Award.

I have just had handed to me an item that I think we will certainly include within the scheme in some way - that is the indenture of R E Bishop to the de Havilland Aircraft Company, Stag Lane Edgware. It is interesting to see the reward he received working for the company, some four and a half pence per hour. The reward we received from him working for the company is incalculable, for the innovative aircraft he designed such as the Mosquito and the Comet have formed a significant mark in the history of British aviation. We are indeed fortunate this evening to have two sons of Mr Bishop present with us.

What I would like to do now is to hand over to Charles Masefield who will be speaking on the Mosquito".

Charles Masefield took the podium:

"Ladies and Gentlemen, Lee. Thank you very much for giving me the task of proposing the toast 'The Mosquito'. I am rather wondering what I should say about the aeroplane after some eight hours solid about it today, so I will bear in mind your kindness in picking me.

Let me start off by answering your first test question of how many first flights were there of the Mosquito? - the answer is 7,781, because each aeroplane only flies once on it's first flight!. You might have noticed that I got that information from this wine bottle that we all have on our tables - we have gone into the wine business should the aircraft business fall on hard times!. Pat Fillingham asked me if this was filled in the Hydraulic Bay here at Hatfield - the answer is yes but I am delighted to say that it has become slightly contaminated with wine!.

As was said at the start of to-day, this week has been remarkable in the history of our nation, because of course the Mosquito will never be 50 again.

I think that there have been one or two happenings outside of Hatfield that we are just hearing about. (Editors Note: this was the week when Margaret Thatcher was replaced by John Major as Prime Minister). I think that the sad events that have befallen our recent Prime Minister may be because when anyone is in a position for a long time the tendency to listen less and less and transmit more and more is difficult to resist. If you turn that back to the aircraft industry, I think one of the great things about de Havilland and certainly about DH himself and his team, is that they did a lot of listening to what the market-place wanted.

It was a very market driven company and a market driven team. I use the term market driven advisedly and not customer driven because one of the great traps is to be customer driven and listen too closely to what the individual customer wants but more assess what the overall market wants.

I think that the Mosquito is a case in point. I do not think that the Royal Air Force would ever come to de Havillands or any other company and say *'build us an aeroplane out of wood, and make sure that it has no armament, we only need two crew and so on'*. The customer would not have actually asked for that. The genius of the concept was that it was recognised that this was something that the customer, the Royal Air force did need. The farsightedness of it all was that this was pioneering a concept, not an aircraft, because today every strike aircraft is just that - a low level, very high speed unarmed two seat strike aircraft - and that was invented by the Mosquito.

Some of the products that followed from here at Hatfield had the same sort of genesis - no customer came to de Havillands and said 'build us a jet airliner'. The airlines had not thought that far ahead and it was again this farsightedness of seeing what the market needed and then taking the gamble of building it.

Tragically with the Trident which followed the Comet, the team for various reasons, mostly I guess financial, were forced to listen to what a customer wanted - and there was the great trap. The customer wanted an aeroplane that was virtually unsaleable elsewhere and when he got to think about, he found that he wanted the aeroplane that the company had wanted to produce.

I think that DH and his team would be pleased to see what is happening at Hatfield and I think also that they would be pleased with this building we are all in today. We have everyone at Hatfield eating in here for lunch every day, so I think the staff have done very well in providing the fare for us tonight, but they are doing this about six or seven times over every day of the week, and a very fine job they do of it.

It was said many times today that the Mosquito was a remarkable aircraft. Mike Ramsden gave us a magnificent summing up, quoting all the other speakers with some of the things that fascinated him. I would like to return the compliment to Mike and quote a few of his phrases of today. I for one will never think of trees as trees again - they will always be natures composites!. Tomorrow when I look down my garden and see nature's composites blowing in the wind I will think gratefully of that phrase Mike.

I always thought of the Mosquito as this brainchild of genius, but I had not realised that it was the world's first composite strike aircraft, nor the world's first 'Stealth' aircraft!. Also, I never realised until today that without its wooden construction - its composite construction - it would not have been the aircraft it was with its power-to-weight ratio, its smooth dragless skin. That to me was a high point. Also that marvellous statement you made "The highest engineering achievement in timber". I loved the Goering quote: "I turn yellow and green with envy when I see the Mosquito. The British knock together a beautiful wooden aircraft which every piano factory over there is making. They have the geniuses, I have the nincompoops". Marvellous.

This aeroplane that went into service, someone actually said twice a night into Germany - that is remarkable in terms of both performance and serviceability. It reminds me of the BEA Captain who landed his Ambassador in Frankfurt in 1953 and who got totally lost taxying in. A rather irate German came on the radio and asked 'Have you never been to Germany before?" The Captain replied rather laconically "Many times old boy, but this is the first time I've landed!" On all his previous occasions he was of course assisting them in the production of their car parks!

I suppose today if that aeroplane was going through Boscombe Down it would look a bit different. I was breathless listening to Eric Brown's tales of hanging on the props with +4lbs of boost on approach at these incredibly low speeds where just one hiccup from either engine could spoil your whole day. Today Boscombe would have insisted on a huge fin and rudder rather like the Tornado - I do not know what it would have done to the performance, but it certainly would have spoiled the classic lines of the aeroplane.

Of course it's marvellous to see right in front of me the aerodynamics table with Richard Clarkson from the original team.

I was asking John Cunningham, sitting on my right, if on all those occasions that he came back to earth at night in a Mosquito whether he had always got one strapped to his backside or whether he was ever forced to vacate the aeroplane. I am happy to say no, he had managed to keep the number of take-offs and landings in his log-book on the Mosquito equal. John never managed that on all aeroplanes, there was an occasion here at Hatfield where John and young Geoffrey de Havilland both came back without a Moth Minor that had not spun very well.

I am also delighted also to see Sir Arthur Marshall here on my table. Sir Arthur, who still goes into work seven days a week including Sundays, I have known since my days at school when I learned to fly on Tiger Moths at Marshalls and then the University Air Squadron. I well remember the wag in the hangar at Marshalls when we drew our parachutes every day how he always used to say '...dont forget, if it doesn't open cross yer left leg over yer right leg!'. And we always used to ask why and he would say '...well it always easier to screw yer out of the ground clockwise!'.

Then of course there was always the old ones like 'If it don't work, bring it back!'.... Personally, I always rather liked the story about the gentleman that leapt out of an aeroplane, but couldn't find the 'D' ring as he hurtled downwards. To his amazement he passed someone hurtling upwards in the opposite direction, so he shouted across to him 'Do you know anything about parachutes?' And the chap shouted back 'No, and I know nothing about gas cookers as well!'.

I would also like to thank all the speakers who did us proud today. I would also like to thank all the organisers, particularly Lee Balthazor and his team, John Edwards and John Saunders and all the others that put in so much effort to ensure that all went well - and to all of you for coming!.

I am delighted that we have Geoffrey Howell, President of the Main Society with us. I know that you are very busy Geoffrey, but thank you for being with us tonight. And also Ron Kennett, Director of the Society. It is marvellous to have Sir Ivor Broom with us, who himself was a great exponent of the Mosquito and Sir Ivor, maybe you can see on the menu there is someone called Anecdotes. I rather hope that we can persuade you to get on your feet and tell us an anecdote or two on the Mosquito. I see as well you have your navigator who of course is also a Broom, but no relation - welcome to you as well sir.

Lee mentioned the Bishop family, and of course we are proud and delighted to see them tonight. I mentioned Richard Clarkson from the original team, but we have also Ralph Hare - very nice to see him. So, you don't want to hear any more from me, thank you very much for coming along and in proposing the toast, I will just read out one further little paragraph from our Mosquito bottle here. Not only were there those 7,781 first flights Lee, but the aircraft entered service not only with the RAF, but also the Royal Navy, the United States Army Air Corps, the Royal Canadian Air Force, the Royal Australian Air Force, the South African Air Force, the Air Forces of France, Russia, China, Norway, Turkey, Israel, Burma, Dominica, Yugoslavia, Belgium, Switzerland, Sweden and Czechoslovakia. I think that is not a bad list of nations and Air Forces to fly this magnificent aeroplane. Ladies and gentlemen, I give you the toast - The Mosquito".

Lee Balthazor took the microphone:
"Can I call upon Mr Geoffrey Howell, President of the Royal Aeronautical Society to respond".

Geoffrey Howell took the podium:
"Thank you very much, it's been a great pleasure to be here this evening, to take part in this event. I am sorry I was not able to be here this morning and the first part of the afternoon, but I would like to congratulate the Hatfield branch in having such an imaginative idea in the first place and clearly they were extremely well supported by Rolls Royce and British Aerospace in setting up this event. When you see all the exhibits and lecturers, it was extremely well done - and extraordinary event. I was also surprised to see the number of people here - it really has been one of the most successful branch events, or event of any sort that I have ever seen. I think there is a very good lesson here on how to set up events.

Clearly, this year is very much a year of nostalgia. The 50th Anniversary of the Mosquito clearly is important to Hatfield and the de Havilland factory. But of course you all must know of the other 50th Anniversaries that are around at this time, ranging from the Battle of Britain and of course early next year there is the 50th Anniversary of the first flight of the Whittle jet. So I think it is possible to say that 50 years ago was an extraordinary period in British aviation when so many different aircraft types and concepts were put into practice - it really was pioneering days in the greatest sense of the word.

We also have to be a forward-looking Society - and in that sense we have been planning ahead and we believe that the Society has got a great future ahead of it, both in this country and as part of the wider European scene and we certainly are making every effort to try and influence our colleagues in Europe to try and move forward with us.

So, to move onto the other area that we are remembering this evening, this creation of the Bishop Award - certainly from the main Society's point of very we have been trying to find ways of encouraging younger people to come into aeronautics. This is a very important objective, for we need every good person we can get to move into the profession in various ways. Again, I must congratulate the Hatfield branch for such an imaginative idea - it is very clear that you have to start very young to catch people, it's not good enough to wait until they get to University - it's at the schools where perhaps more needs to be done. I am very pleased therefore that they have introduced this scheme.

In fact I have brought with me tonight the main Society's contribution from our Education Committee's trust to this project - here is a £500 cheque, which I gather matches a similar amount that was donated by the Branch and some of the sponsors. So with this I would first of all like to thank British Aerospace for hosting this dinner tonight and for the branch for inviting all the guests tonight and finally to hand this cheque to the Chairman of the Hatfield branch towards this very worthwhile cause. Thank you very much".

Lee Balthazor thanked Geoffrey Howell for the donation and then moved on to present a small memento to each of the lecturers.

From Sir Ivor Broom:
Perhaps I can just pick up something that Charles said earlier. Yes, we did send Mosquitoes to Berlin twice in one night - with different crews. In fact Tommy and I were on the second wave and I think that is not only a tribute to the Mosquito, but one must not forget the Groundcrew. They turned those aircraft around rapidly, got them loaded up again and off we went.

This rascal here (indicating his navigator Tommy Broom) with the same name as myself did his first operational sorties in France in September 1939 and did his last one with me in April 1945 - I do not think that many people had that sort of span of operations. I will tell you a story about him. We were on Berlin one night and it was one of those unfortunate nights when we were picked up by the searchlights very early on the run-in. He by then was down in the nose and we were picked up about seven minutes before we got to the target and held for about another seven minutes, so we were illuminated for about fourteen minutes in all. I'd thrown the thing all over the sky and eventually we were in darkness out of the searchlights so I said to him, who was still falling about in the nose 'Give me a course for home'. Now Tommy Broom is a very practical chap - he said 'Steer West with a dash of North until I get myself sorted out!'

From an unidentified speaker: "DZ353, one of the most famous of Mosquitoes was flown by a very good drinking friend of mine, Roy Ralston, whose Navigator was Sid Leyton. We used to drink in the 'White Horse' at Ipswich every other Saturday night. Apparently, as many of you will know, in the Mosquito, over the tunnel where the control cables go back to the tail there is a device called the saddle tank which was put there to receive the contents of any calls to nature. As the Navigator/Bomb Aimer sat back a bit - half a pace to the right, half a pace to the rear - the pilot could not always see what was happening. Sid was feeling a little uncomfortable, so undid all the necessary zips in his flying suit and got hold of this rather large flask with a deathly rat-trap spring on the top. Now if you did not control that, you were really in trouble! It was held in a Terry Clip, Sid made a grab, yanked it out rather too heavily and the rubber pipe flipped off the stub-pipe on the saddle tank, did a snake up in the air and landed in the top of Roy's flying boot. The story really started because Roy could never understand why he flew all the way to Germany and back with his right foot absolutely frozen solid!"

Captain Eric Brown: "I think that this story appertains up to a point to the lecture I gave earlier today. You may remember that the Mosquito had a very vicious power stall. One of the things we did during this series of tests was to fit a trailing static line to the aircraft, which was really about 100ft of rubber tube that hung under the aircraft with a very small thing like a 12lb bomb on the end. This was to get an accurate reading of the airspeed outside any turbulent flow.

During one particular test we were trying to hold the aircraft up as much as possible by use of aileron so that it wouldn't go to early - but when it did go, it really went, and it went over completely inverted and this rubber tube wrapped itself around the tail. We came back and landed with no problem and the machine was left on the tarmac for about 24 hours for we wanted a series of photographs of the event. During that period one of our splendid Ministers of State visited Farnborough with his wife and she came along and stood looking at the Mosquito. She said 'Darling, you told me that this carried a large bomb and it was carried under the aircraft, not on top!"

Unidentified Speaker:"It was quite all right for you down there in the front looking at everything happening, but what about the poor wretched observer who was sat in the rear fuselage who let the thing out, he didn't know what was going on - you at least could see! But back in the rear fuselage, now that was very exciting!"

Charles Masefield: "I was going to tell the anecdote of the Mosquito pilot who went in for his bacon, sausages and eggs that were the tradition. He cut into his sausage, took a mouthful then spat it out. He turned to the Steward and said 'Steward!, this sausage tastes like bloody sawdust - I joined the Air Force to fly the Mosquito, not eat the bloody thing!'"

Bill Baird: "Well I think that my talk, or anecdote generally, takes about fifty minutes - and that's only if I'm feeling well! I think that the point is there came a time when I was carting about Mosquito W4050 all over the place. Walter Goldsmith, who had bought Salisbury Hall asked me if he could find enough money to buy a hangar, would we let him have the Mosquito. I said yes. We had managed to get the aircraft out of the Works Directors eye, for he had came into my office and ordered me to 'Burn the damn thing, it's a nuisance!' So we got it outside and into the Fiddlebridge Stores.

In due course Walter came back to me and said that he was very sorry, but he could not raise the money to buy this hangar he thought he'd got. He had been talking to the trustees that ran a Family Trust and they wouldn't let him have the capital. He asked could de Havilland's do anything?' I went for a word with Sir Geoffrey, and he said "I think you had better have a word with Wilfred'. Well, Wilfred happened to be Mr Nixon, the Chairman. So I went and saw Mr Nixon. He was the gentleman who, I suppose you will remember, used to recover the company from terrible financial difficulties. He asked me what I wanted.

"Would the company finance the purchase of this hangar?' I asked. 'No' was the reply - he was quite concessional about it. I then played what I thought was my trump card by saying 'We can go to a public subscription, but wouldn't it be bad if the company is not mentioned?'. He said 'No'. This mono-syllabic conversation began to get me down, so I went back to my office.

Not long after, the Director who had told me to 'burn the damn thing' came in, sat opposite me and said 'I understand you want to buy a hangar to house the ashes of the aircraft I told you to burn'. At that stage I was not listening, I was trying to work out what my redundancy pay would be! Thank you".

Unidentified Speaker: "This is connected with the very early days of Pathfinders when Air Vice Marshal Bennett was a Group Captain during the formation of the Pathfinder Force. We had 109 Squadron there and a story went around that was never really confirmed that D.C.T. Bennett and this rather 'ace' navigator of ours, a chap called Anderson, got themselves loose from Wyton one night in a Mosquito and they disappeared for about three of four hours.

Nobody quite knew where they went, but rumour had it that they landed at Kinloss, nipped into flying control, had a quick look at the station routine orders to find where they were and then came back home again!"

Richard Clarkson: "I think that it is cruelty to old men to twist my arm to make me get up here, but I suppose I have to earn my dinner! There are two things I remember from the very very early days... As we have been told to-day, the Mosquito was not 'respectable' until the Ministry had measured its speed, and Mike Ramsden told us how it happened... But there are things connected with some of these events that you will never hear in a lecture theatre, or ever read in a book.

The party went down there (to Boscombe Down) - Geoffrey de Havilland, Fred Plumb, who built the Mosquito, a couple of Rolls Royce mechanics, me and my Flight Engineer and maybe one or two others. We stayed at the George in Amesbury. When they had weighed, measured, balanced and sorted out the Mosquito it came to the day to fly it. Boscombe Down ground crew tried to start the engines and after this had been going on for a very long time Allen Wheeler said "Well, it's lunchtime now, we had better go to lunch...' so everybody went to lunch, but before we got off the aerodrome the two Rolls Royce people who were with us in our party leapt into the car before we could, started it and got around the corner!. Everybody laughed about it!

The next day everyone was ready to measure the speed, this was the crucial part of the exercise. But unfortunately this was a Sunday - and a sports day. It was gin clear - a perfect day for performance measurement, but no, the Station were having their Sports Day. We could not quite understand this - we had been working seven, eight days a week - we thought there was a war on!.

So I went with my Flight Engineer (who also liked a pint) and we spent the day taking the waters up and down the Avon valley. In those days, every little town had its brewery and every pub was different, so it turned out a lovely day!

On the Monday, when we knew the speed and what it implied, Geoffrey de Havilland said '... a party!, we must have a party at the George!' We invited Gordon Slade, Allen Wheelright (Allen Wheeler) and Fred Rouse to the party, and of course it went right out of hand - it went absolutely out of hand. I was supposed to be the chap that was capable of keeping it in bounds, but it was quite impossible!

Allen Wheeler never forgot this. When we used to meet from time to time we always said 'Do you remember that party at the George...?'. Fred Plumb, - some of us remember him', was a podgy little man with squint eyes - a very unprepossessing chap - when the party got really rough he made a pass at the landlord's wife, Geoffrey de Havilland was found to be running up and down the corridor with nothing on... And er.. Well you have to remember there was a lot of pent-up something that had to be released here. We knew that it was a terrific occasion!

The landlord said 'de Havillands - out of the George!. No de Havilland people shall come in the George at Amesbury ever more!" So that was it - we were out.

Then I think it was the nexy day when the Mosquito broke its back. Fred Plumb hurried back to Hatfield to see about getting it mended. The first person that he met in the passage was the Chairman, Mr Butler. he said "Fred Plumb! How's the Mosquito going?' Fred said '...broken its back!' The Chairman reeled, his eyes popped out of his head and he staggered about the place... and that was that.

The other little thing, was on one of the very early flights of the prototype Mosquito here. In those days the first flight could be a very intimate thing. You didn't know what might go wrong and you kept very quiet about it. The prototype was placed right at the far end, nearest the end hangar. It was a November day with snow flurries and things, the odd shower and it was cold. I suppose Sir Geoffrey was there, Mr Walker..., Bish would have been there and the odd ground crew and other such people there. Probably Guy Gardner was there because Bish deputed Guy Gardner (I think he's around here somewhere...) to keep an eye on those aerodynamicists and test pilots and see what they are doing.. Generally as we've heard, John Walker was in the second seat. Well now, when the aeroplane taxied in and as you know the exit was down in the floor. Some chap came up with a ladder or something to let them out...

Well I have never until this day, and I still don't know - perhaps I have forgotten, perhaps I did know - I don't know why Geoffrey didn't tell the chap down below what was on the floor of the Mosquito. This chap came up and opened the floor and of course there was about two feet of hydraulic oil or something there, and of course he got anointed. Everyone absolutely howled with laughter..."

Unidentified speaker: "Speaking of the differences between a lot of lines on a piece of paper and an object flying through the air is due to the men, and in some cases later on women, who interpreted those lines and made the thing out of wood and metal. I was one of the early ones at Salisbury Hall. I arrived the first week in January with my mate Harry who is also here tonight - there's not many of us left. I was one of the youngest, there were some there that were old enough to be my father, and they are sadly no longer with us.

When we arrived, the whole lot was covered with snow - we turned the corner and we saw a hangar. In front of the hangar was some men playing football. We were surprised, "Why football?" "Go and clock in and then come out, cos it's so cold we play football until half-past eight to get warm". We did that and opened the wicket gate in the hangar.

We had a hangar front, a left hand and right hand wall and about three-eighths of a back wall. They couldn't lay any more bricks, so they covered it up with bits of tin and canvas. We had roughly two thirds of a roof. The whole lot, all our benches, all our machines were covered with a layer of snow. We had no heat, we had no water, that had to be fetched from the house. We had no loo - the loo was a pit dug in the field with a post across it and some corrugated iron around it. Those of you that are familiar with the "Decameron' will understand why we were loathe to use it!

Hatfield had sent over a urn with two elements burnt out - the third didn't see why it should work if the other two weren't. We had a lot of power cuts, and of course in our ignorance we said, 'Ah well, where's the canteen?' - "Hah, Hah, hah". 'Well. what time's the tea-break?' "Ah, now that's a point - we run a book on that! We put a mug of water in the urn for each person that's here. As there's four more here today, that means four more cups of water, so we'll make a fresh book' The record, if my memory serves me right was twenty to twelve when the urn boiled - teas were a bit late.

But we soldiered on. We gradually got some water, we got a loo and we began to make aeroplanes. Asbestos-clad buildings are a bit like a fifty bob suit - they fit where they touch!. We spent a lot of time shoving felt, straw and anything we could get hold of in the cracks. Eventually we got a reasonable draught-proof building without any heat. We only got heat, I'm convinced, because the glue would not set. I think if I remember rightly it's got to be 54 degrees before the glue would set - it wouldn't set so they put some heat in.

But we survived, and there's one important point that I want to make tonight. I understand that at that time we created a world record for producing a prototype from the drawing board to flying. We actually got a memo from the firm which we put up on the clock congratulating us on it. I don't know whether you know that Mr Chairman and I also don't know if the record has ever been beaten - I would like to know for there was a lot of blood, sweat and tears went into that and we were very very proud to have been part of it. Thank you".

Ron Clear: "I will make this as short as I possibly can. Perhaps my association with the Mosquito was a little unique in that the very first time I flew one was from Thorney Island to Portsmouth. I had only the Pilots Notes to look at prior to flying it and that aeroplane I have learned was in fact DZ555/G - one of the Highball aeroplanes that was being taken into

Portsmouth to be modified for the spinning mine.

Briefly, I accompanied Bob Milne, who was Chief Pilot at Portsmouth at that time. The idea was that he would take the first aircraft, and if he hadn't returned in thirty minutes, I was to take-off and take mine over to Portsmouth. He never returned, so I started up, took off and headed for Portsmouth. Upon my arrival in the circuit, I noticed Bob coming in on a normal circuit with everything looking perfectly well. His touch-down was so close to the boundary that I was totally amazed at the very short landing run. I came round in due course thinking therefore that the field was very adequate for the Mosquito. I came in at a speed that was a little bit fast and found that I could not land the aeroplane in the three-point attitude to get the aerodynamic drag that was required for that short field. As a result I had to do an overshoot half way across the field and ran into this very heavy swing that developed that Captain Brown referred to in his lecture on a overshoot from a carrier.

I then climbed up to do a series of stalls in the aeroplane and generally discovered that I could come in somewhat slower and in due course successfully made a reasonable landing.

Later, when I spoke to Bob Milne on the ground about it - I said how on earth did you make such a short landing? The answer was 'Well, perhaps put it down to the difference between the men and the boys!' I never did understand how he never achieved on subsequent tests anything like that landing distance again.

It was only when these three aircraft were modified, delivered and the contract was finished that one night I asked him again how such a short landing happened. He told me that when he was talking off from Thorney Island he had been rushed in his take-off checks and had missed noticing that the strap that held the overhead escape hatch was not locked. During the take-off this hatch had lifted off. He then felt that the only thing to do before going into Portsmouth was to check the stall to see if the stalling speed had increased due to the effect of the missing hatch and possibly a loss of lift on the centre section. On checking the stall he discovered that the airflow was disturbed over the top of the canopy which caused the top of his flying helmet to 'burble' as soon as he got to the stall. He realised of course that now he had a built-in stall warning device, so simply made his approach using the throttle to just keep off this 'helmet burble' to make what is possibly the shortest ever landing made in a Mosquito!. Thank you".

Guy Bristow: "I worked the other side of the aerodrome on engine testing. This is one side you have not talked about today - you have to have an engine in the aeroplane, and Halford's team was led by the man that put most of your aeroplanes in the air! I was a member of that team and we put the Albatross in the air with the Gypsy Twelve, the Comet with the Gipsy Sixes, the later Comet with the Ghosts, the SAAB J29 - the Swedish fighter in the air, across in the States the Shooting Star... The NF.15... we were busy, but not all our projects finished because of government cuts in different counties.

I have enjoyed a life here since 1935, developing engines for you chaps and I would like to say on Major Halford's part - he is dead now, and so is Moult, his assistant - that they did a wonderful job and helped you to get what you did here in the way of wonderful aeroplanes. Thank you".

Unidentified Speaker: "Ladies and Gentlemen, having been involved production wise on the Mosquito since September 1939 when I was shipped to Salisbury Hall by Mr Plumb with five other colleagues to build the mock-ups in the servants hall - that was before the hangar was built; the design team were there, but we were the only production people.

Well, the hangar was built and I went in the hangar and built several jigs and part of the mould that built the fuselage. Then I was transferred back to Hatfield to begin organising the production jigs for people, and that was the beginning of the Aero Tools, which some here tonight might remember.

In 1942 I said to my friends in Flight Test 'I've been on this god-dammed aeroplane all these years - can I get a flight in the thing?' 'We'll fix it' they said. A couple of days later I had a telephone call from Flight Test 'Aeroplane waiting for you, quick'. Round I went and John de Havilland was already sitting in the aeroplane. They stuffed me up the opening and I sat on the spar...

Well, the aircraft was a PR machine, and I saw St Albans from just about every attitude possible - for three quarters of an hour I never knew that an aircraft could do such things!. Anyway, we got down eventually, I dropped out of that doorway and went to the small room and for about an hour I didn't know if I was standing, sitting, on my head or my knees!.

The next day they said 'Would you like another flight?' That was my friends in Flight Test!"

Fig.74: "Berlin and back and in the Bar before it closes!" Wing Commander Ivor Broom takes off from an East Anglian Airfied in a Light Night Striking Force Mosquito

CHAPTER THIRTEEN

25 NOVEMBER 1990 - AN OCCASION TO REMEMBER!

Ian Thirsk - De Havilland Aircraft Museum

The weekend of 24/25 November 1990 fell into two distinct days - the Saturday, the day of the symposium and the Sunday, the actual 50th Anniversary which was the day the the de Havilland Aircraft Museum held their celebrations and 'unveiled' TA634, their B.Mk.35 after a ten year restoration programme. Ian Thirsk, Aircraft Restoration Manager of the Collection, takes up the story of the planning, the roll-out and the day itself...

"It was the de Havilland Mosquito's 50th birthday and it had to be celebrated. We felt it was up to us to do something special - not only did we want to do it, but fellow Mosquito devotees the world over were depending upon us!. Looking back now, I believe we succeeded admirably - there was a unique atmosphere at Salisbury Hall on the day, the like of which I have never experienced before.

The Mosquito Aircraft Museum had long been aware that W4050's "50th" was an occasion which had to be marked - the fact that W4050 is still with us made it all the more significant. Of the four prototypes of the RAF's most famous aircraft of the Second World War - the Spitfire, Hurricane, Lancaster and Mosquito, only the Mosquito survived - truly then, W4050 is totally unique.

Serious planning for the event began in the latter part of 1989. The BAe Mosquito RR299 was 'booked' at this time, as she would obviously play a major part in the proceedings (The Museum has a long association with '299, and has provided spares support for over 20 years). As restoration work on our own Mosquito B.Mk.35 TA634 was nearing completion, it seemed sensible to try for a post-restoration 'roll-out', although there was still a lot of outstanding work to do.

It also seemed very important to try and hold the celebration on the actual day of the anniversary, November 25th. There was some opposition to this initially, weather conditions could hardly be guaranteed, and it was likely to be cold and wet. Fair enough I suppose, but the actual date fell on a weekend - a marvellous opportunity for a historically poignant day!. As it transpired, weather conditions did nearly interrupt proceedings but someone up there smiled on us!.

By January 1990 a rough format for the day had been worked out. We would invite ex-Mosquito Designers, Production Workers, Air and Ground crews as well as our own Museum workers. TA634 would be rolled out in all her glory, there would be a buffet lunch followed by a demonstration of RR299.

At this time we were contacted by the Hatfield branch of the Royal Aeronautical Society, who informed us that they were holding a "Mosquito Symposium" at BAe Hatfield on 24 November. Several significant guest speakers had been invited to recount their

Mosquito days, including John Cunningham, Pat Fillingham and Captain Eric Brown. Why didn't we link with Hatfield RAeS to present a joint event?. This seemed a very good idea. so we consented. Throughout 1990 we held regular meetings with John Edwards and John Saunders, which proved to be of great mutual benefit.

The Mosquito prototype W4050 would really be the star of the day. Unfortunately, we could not roll the aircraft out of her current Robin hangar, but much work was conducted to ensure that she looked her best on the day. This was undertaken by Alan Brackley of the Museum's Mosquito Team. Alan re-painted the prototypes original manufacturers Class 'B' registration of EO234 on the starboard side of the fuselage - the prototype made her first flight in these markings, and Alan's handiwork certainly confused a number of people!.

The Shuttleworth Trust then contacted me to ask whether we had considered the DH88 Comet Racer's participation in the event - things were beginning to come together.

As the event was going to include a number of flying demonstrations, we would have to obtain permission from the Civil Aviation Authority - a fairly lengthy process but one that we are well acquainted with due to our annual 'Open Weekend' and flying display. I am grateful to Alan Brackley for his normal competent handling of the issue.

Throughout the year preparations got underway at Salisbury Hall. Work on TA634 was frantic in order to prepare her for re-painting. By September she proudly wore the camouflage finish she had been rolled out in 45 years earlier (Fig.75). By October she was ready, enabling us to concentrate on other areas, but until 25 November she remained draped in plastic sheeting in order to deter photographers getting pictures until THE day!.

Publicity would be paramount and was handled by Museum member Paul Doyle, who ensured that national as well as local media knew what was going on. By September we were

Fig.75: September 1990 and now resplendant in her new paintwork under the plastic sheeting, TA634 has her serial re-applied. (Photo: De Havilland Aircraft Museum).

receiving letters and phone calls from ex-Mossie types wishing to attend - I have to thank Museum Registrar Harry Rolfe for his superhuman endurance!.

The final two weeks leading up to the event were fraught with problems to overcome and work to do - special thanks must go to all our regular Museum members: special mention must be made to two of our lady members who made the 'DE HAVILLAND MOSQUITO 1940-1990' banner that hung over the hangar mouth and our regular car-parking team led by Ian Rumney who prepared the ground for battle!.

By this time the programme had been finalised: at 1130hrs Museum Chairman Bill Baird would make a welcoming speech in W4050's hangar and give a brief resume of how the aircraft survived, A 1200hrs TA634 would be rolled out and accepted on behalf of the Museum by John Cunningham. At 1230hrs Mosquito RR299 flown by John Sadler and the Comet G-ACSS flown by George Ellis would make a formation flypast before breaking off for individual displays. At 1300hrs a buffet lunch would be served by Sally Darnell and her staff of Garden City Cooks.

As most of our members were attending the Symposium on Saturday, many took Friday 23rd November off work to ensure that all would be ready. The stage was set...

The great day arrives!

By 0830 everyone was on site and wondering what the next few hours would bring. I remember feeling extremely anxious - had I forgotten something, how would we be received, what about gatecrashers, would the Mossie get through...?

Final touches were being made to the hangar displays, and the banner fluttered proudly in the breeze as Alan Brackley and David Bray placed the display axis markers in the fields. Nevertheless, it was still grey and misty - please give us sunshine!

By 1030 most of our guests had arrived. Ian Rumney's team coped admirably with the car parking whilst the BAe security staff dealt firmly with a number of gatecrashers. John Sadler phoned from Chester to say that he was still fog-bound and therefore could not make the 1230 slot, but he would try later.

We had a very distinguished gathering, including Richard Clarkson of the original design team, Air Chief Marshal Sir Ivor Broom and his Navigator, Group Captain 'Slim' Somerville ex-109 Squadron, Squadron Leader Terry Kearns ex-617 Squadron and the sons of R. E. Bishops, the Chief Designer. Also present was Mrs Carla Rowland, widow of the late Flt. Lt Peter Rowland of 105 Squadron (the man who collected the chimney pot in the nose of his Mosquito), Ron Clear, ex-Hatfield Test and RR299 pilot, George Aird, who delivered Kermit Weeks' Mosquito B.Mk.35 RS712 to Miami in 1987, plus many more. There were crews from 684 Sqn, 162, 571, 627, 464, 139... it was overwhelming, absolutely marvellous!. The day really belonged to these people and it was wonderful to witness their obvious pleasure in renewing their acquaintance with the 'wooden wonder'!.

The telephone never stopped ringing, television crews wanted interviews and everybody was asking questions.

Bill Baird began his speech in the Robin hangar and the Mosquito Team's big moment was approaching. Richard Tyler removed the plastic sheeting and Paul Doyle began his crowd-control act - then the sun began to shine!

On the stroke of mid-day TA634 began to roll out of the hangar (Fig.76). It was as if

Fig.76: The great moment!. TA634 is rolled out in front of the waiting crowd.
(Photo: De Havilland Aircraft Museum).

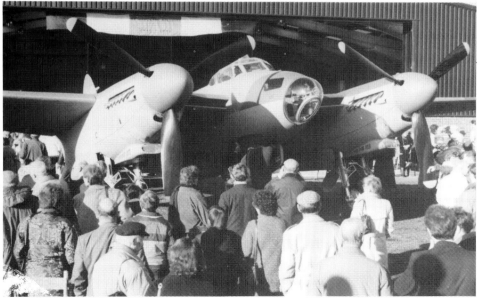

Fig.77: After the ceremony the team's handiwork was available for inspection by the admiring
crowd (Photo: De Havilland Aircraft Museum).

she knew!. Normally we have problems with the concrete ramp, but this time she came out with ease. We were conscious of the applause, the cameras and the videos everywhere. John Cunningham accepted the aircraft on behalf of the Museum and then made a short speech to the memory of all those who built, serviced and flew the Mosquito.

Then came another highlight - the Comet Racer, flown with gusto by George Ellis. We were very grateful to the Shuttleworth Trust for allowing this important aircraft (so significant to the Mosquito story) to participate in the event.

I was still concerned about John Sadler and RR299 when he phoned again - He was going to have another go! John was doing his utmost for us - if this had been any other occasion the aircraft would have stayed firmly on the ground!.

In the meantime our guests were sampling the excellent buffet lunch and admiring TA634 (Fig.77). Anglia Television were interviewing John Cunningham and I was trying to talk to about twelve people at once. I was wondering how John Sadler was getting on when someone picked him up on an airband radio talking to Luton ATC - Five minutes later it was announced that the Mosquito was running in.

It suddenly went very quiet, but that was soon broken by the sound of a pair of Merlins as John passed over the M25 and across the fields behind the Museum. Seeing the Mosquito perform always sends shivers down the spine and this was no exception - there followed one of the most memorable displays we have ever had. John flew up the fields towards the Museum before breaking off into a series of smooth and graceful flypasts. The Merlins sounded beautiful as John treated our guests to a king-sized display which left more than a few with moist eyes. As he departed back for Chester he waggled the wings in salute. As our commentator Philip Birtles said at the time "What a finale to a fantastic weekend..."

After the day we received wonderful coverage in the press - we also received a number of wonderful 'thank you' letters from ex-Mossie crews who attended. I would like to close with an extract from just one that seemed to make it all worthwhile...

"For 'oldies' like us, nostalgia is the name of the game, and for many of us it was grand to talk over old time, to exchange experiences and to 'shoot our lines'. Do you recall the hush when it was announced the Mosquito was approaching?. Then came the thrill of the fly-over, the culmination of a marvellous afternoon. There were many, like me, who envied the pilot and would have loved to be up there with him. He gave us a grand display and for a few minutes everything else was forgotten and we were young again, standing on the dispersal back at the Squadron. It was the more significant when the B.35 was rolled out, since it was in our old squadron's livery - 8K - 571 Squadron".

Fig.78: TA634, with TK607 'W' in the background whilst flying with the Armament Practice Station (APS) around 1956. (Photo: De Havilland Aircraft Museum)

Fig.79: TA634 with No. 3 CAACU on 11 September 1963.
(Photo: De Havilland Aircraft Museum).

Fig.80: TA634 undergoing maintenance in preparation at Speke during June 1968 for the film *'Mosquito Squadron'* (Photo: De Havilland Aircraft Museum)

The history of the aircraft and its restoration...

The Mosquito B.Mk.35 was the ultimate bomber version of the classic Mosquito design. It was a direct development of the B.Mk.XVI, powered by a pair of Rolls Royce Merlin 113/114 engines, each developing 1,760h.p. with a maximum speed of 422 mph. The type made its first flight on 12 March 1945, too late to see war service.

The Museum's example, TA634 was built at Hatfield in April 1945 and was delivered to 27MU on 14 April 1945, to remain in storage for the next seven years, when it was selected for conversion to target-tug configuration (TT.Mk.35) by Brooklands Aviation at Sywell. It was delivered to them on 22 February 1952 for removal of all its bomber equipment and a ML Type G wind-driven winch was fitted in the bomb-bay. Cable guards were positioned around the tail surfaces and the aircraft's camouflage scheme was replaced with an overall silver scheme with black and yellow stripes on the undersurfaces. Five months later it was delivered to 22 MU at Silloth for further storage.

TA634 was delivered to 4 CAACU at Llandow on 31 December 1954 to start its target-towing career, but was back in storage again by July 1954, this time with 38 MU. On 12 March 1956 it was delivered to the Armament Practice Station (APS) on the island of Sylt, part of the Headquarters, 2nd Tactical Air Force (Fig.78) and later moved to Ahlhorn and Schelswigland, towing drogues over the Todendorf ranges off the Baltic Coast.

On 26 June 1957 the aircraft was flown back to 27 MU fur further storage until 10

September 1959 when it went to 3 CAACU at Exeter (Fig.79), receiving the code '53'. Here it remained and took part in the last official flypast of Mosquitoes over Exeter. All except two found their way to Bovingdon to take part in the film 633 Squadron - the two that did not were RR299 and TA634.

The Merseyside Society of Aviation Enthusiasts had plans to obtain a Mosquito for preservation, and persuaded the airport committee to spend £720 to purchase TA634 which would then be displayed at the airport entrance. All target towing gear was removed and the aircraft was flown to Speke on 6 November 1963, but plans fell through and the aircraft was stored in hangars 39 and 50 until 1968, when it landed the starring role in *Mosquito Squadron* (Fig.80), the sequel to *633 Squadron* . The aircraft was fully inspected and some items replaced or removed. Finally, on 12 July 1968 TA634 received a Permit to fly and was allocated the civilian registration G-AWJV. After filming there were plans to keep the machine airworthy, but they fell through and the aircraft languished at Speke until October 1970 when the Liverpool Corporation donated the aircraft to the Mosquito Aircraft Museum. On 15 May 1971 the Mosquito was officially accepted by the Museum and dedicated as a memorial to Group Captain P.C.Pickard who led the famous Amiens Prison raid on 18 February 1944 in Mosquito FB.Mk.VI HX922.

Thus began a very hard nine years of outdoor display at Salisbury Hall. Although TA634 was well looked after by the Museum members, it was inevitable that deterioration would set in and any form of preservation would be a battle, for wooden aeroplanes do not

Fig.81: Just as work began - the aircraft is moved into the new hangar and dismantling begins. The handwritten caption on the rear of this photo asked "Whose idea was it anyway?"

Fig.82:The team hard at work re-fitting the Port Nacelle

like being left out in the open. Most affected was the fabric covering which split, allowing water into the wooden structure underneath. Despite strenuous efforts by Stuart Howe, John Oldacre and Walter Goldsmith, by the mid-1970's it was obvious that permanent hangarage would be needed, so in 1977 a massive public appeal was launched, both for TA634 and other aircraft in the Museums care. The appeal was successful and the hangar was erected in stages as the funds came in. By October 1980 TA634 was rolled under cover after ten years in the open (Fig.81).

In the summer of 1981 a new team was formed to restore TA634, including Peter Waxham, Derek Purchase, Peter Mitchell, Stuart Howe and myself. After discussion it was decided that the restoration would have two aims: to strip down the airframe and rebuild and replace where required, at the same time converting the aircraft back from a target-tug to its original bomber status. All the work was undertaken by members on a voluntary basis, working in their spare time. The first task was to remove the fabric - underneath, the structure was in surprisingly good condition, with very few signs of water damage, so attention was next turned to removal and refurbishment of all metal components.

By now the team had been joined by David Bray and Alan Brackley. TA634's original tailcone had collapsed after prolonged exposure to the elements, so a new one was fabricated by Paul Doyle. An original, unused 'Perspex' nose was fitted in 1988 after it was found by Tony Agar in a Scottish scrapyard!. British Aerospace Hatfield and Chester produced new moldings for the nose windows. In 1988 the Imperial War Museum donated a Merlin 114 in

Fig.83: The machine starts to come together. Now back on its undercarriage with one engine and propeller installed suring January 1989. (Photo: De Haviland Aircraft Museum)

return for help with their own B.Mk.35.

Peter Waxham made a splendid job of repairing the gash in the leading edge of the starboard wing, whilst Dennis Scuffell repaired the soggy balsa in the nose. Peter and Dennis also carried out the repairs to the wing trailing edges, port wingtip and also refurbished the flaps, tailplane and bomb doors (Fig.82). To re-fabric the aircraft took two summers to achieve. The undercarriage was beautifully refurbished by Bill Forbes, along with the engine nacelles, elevators, spinners and one propeller (Fig.83).

Work progressed, and in 1988 the aircraft received the Scania Transport Trust Award for its restoration.

By August 1990 TA634 was ready for repainting - done with such skill by Clive Denney of Historic Aircraft Ltd in the standard day bomber finish with the markings of '8K-K' as originally worn by a B.Mk.XVI ML963 of 571 Squadron, Light Night Striking Force.

Many people have come and gone in the team, but David, Alan and myself, latterly joined by Richard Tyler, Ray Bernard and Bruce Gordon have always formed the core of such a hard working, dedicated team.

For anyone requiring further information, or would like to join us, please write to:-
The De havilland Aircraft Museum, P.O.Box 107 London Colney, Herts.

CHAPTER FOURTEEN

COME ON DOWN - THE WEATHER'S FINE!
John Sadler - Pilot, BAe Mosquito RR299

John Sadler regularly flew the British Aerospace Mosquito T.Mk.III RR299 at airshows throughout the summer months. The machine is lovingly maintained in airworthy condition by a small number of BAe employees at the Chester site.

The aircraft, a 1945 Leavesden-built T.Mk. III training machine has a long, but not very interesting service history, being transferred through a number of Maintenance and Operational Training Units. However, in December 1945 it did serve in the Middle East, including a year in Aden. Like many of the surviving Mosquitoes, the aircraft served with 3 Civil Anti Aircraft Co-Operation Unit at Exeter, finally being declared surplus to requirements in March 1963 and transferred to de Havillands. She received her civilian Certificate of Registration (as G-ASKH) on Spetember 9th 1965. The aircraft became a film star in *633 Squadron* and its sequel *Mosquito Squadron* during the 1960's.

It was planned that the aircraft would appear at Hatfield on the day of the Symposium, but events sometimes do not turn out as planned, as John Sadler recalls...

"I stared gloomily over the nose to the point where the cloud merged impenetrably with the rising ground. it cannot have been more than four miles away and we were approaching it at three miles a minute. I sighed and pulled the Mosquito into a tight turn to the left, the wing-tips scoring white trails of condensation over the outskirts of Stoke and headed back, frustrated to Hawarden.

The 50th Anniversary of the first flight had been celebrated with a hangar party on the Friday. We had hoped to wind up the day with a graduation fly-past at Church Fenton where, coincidentally, one of our guests, John Norris, had operated Mosquitoes during the war. The aeroplane would then have flown to Hatfield, but the weather had deteriorated during the day, so we stayed on the ground. By this time a clock had begun counting down in my mind; we didn't want to let down the Hatfield people who had planned a comprehensive weekend of lectures, social functions and flying displays. Since we could not fly on the Friday, 'Plan B' was to get there early on the Saturday.

I am not normally one to bend the rules, especially those that have been developed in the light of experience to keep us safe in the air, but I found myself wrestling with the temptation that weekend. The Visual Flight Rules are simple - if your plane is not equipped for blind flying you must be able to see enough to tell up from down, to navigate and to avoid other aircraft. Our Mosquito is very much a VFR aeroplane and although the weather was reasonable at Hatfield, it was certainly anything but around Hawarden.

By Saturday, a deep depression had moved in from the Atlantic and parked a thick, wet blanket of cloud over the Midlands. We were obviously in for a slow start. Plan B became Plan C: get there any time Saturday. By late morning you could see the high ground to the Welsh side of the airfield, so I decided to give it a go. Shortly after take-off I was doing my U-turn over Stoke. So far Plans A, B and C had failed; but we were not discouraged - there were still twenty three letters to go!.

Sunday morning dawned with a lighter shade of grey and even the odd streak of light in the sky. But the Airmet forcast again provided little comfort; the low had settled over England. I came into the office and made a few phone calls. The Midlands airfields were way below visual conditions but at least Hatfield showed promise. If the cloud was not as thick as expected and Birmingham Radar could help with navigation above it, there was a chance. Birmingham rang back and said that a pilot had reported the cloud tops in their area as 2,500ft with clear sky above. This was much better than forcast, so I rang Salisbury Hall to say that we were on our way again. We could not now arrive in time to join the Comet Racer over Salisbury Hall as planned, so we settled for going direct to the display and come straight back.

We took off into a milky sky and groped towards Poulton disused airfield whence my track to Birmingham started. Over Poulton I carefully set the heading and started the stop-watch. Below us a small circle of Cheshire slid past as though lit up in the gloom by an usherette's torch. After a couple of minutes I recognised The Egerton Arms. Satisfied that we were on track, I pulled up steeply, keeping a careful eye open for icing. "Just think..." I said to Steve Watson, "...down there more sensible people than us are soaking up their lunchtime Bass". Suddenly we broke clear of the overcast and the cockpit brightened in the oblique sunshine.

Six minutes from Poulton we saw Tern Hill through a gap in the cloud. I called Birmingham Radar, not expecting to be picked up as we were still quite low, a good 30 miles off and the Mosquito is, after all, the original stealth bomber. But they found us and helped us cheerfully on our way. At a time when the BBC were reporting chaotic conditions on the M6 motorway, we were motoring along serenely less than a mile above it all in dazzling sunshine.

As we passed Luton, the cloud below broke up and thinned out so that by Hatfield the sky was clear and the Home Counties stretched before us. Salisbury Hall from above looks a pretty inadequate airfield and a very unlikely spot for a first flight. In preparation for the display, Steve opened the Radiator Flaps while I set the RPM and Boost to a sporting 2,400/+4 . In the cool November air the old aeroplane shivered to life.

Descending into a non-airfield display site is a time for extra vigilance - a time to pick up the markers and spot the hazards, like the embankment of the M25 at the eastern end. Only on the second run did I notice the enclosure full of white-haired veterans looking for all the world like a field full of daisies. many had probably not seen a Mosquito in years and I felt distinctly privileged to be bringing the aeroplane to them.

On the return trip Birmingham extracted payment for their assistance by requesting a low fly-past which helped me by threading us through the last block of controlled airspace before Chester. Soon we were again navigating by braille through the gloom over the Dee valley. A glimpse of the Red House was the cue for a sharp turn left which brought us shortly over the airfield. "Time for a beer or three" said Steve as we taxied in. "Yes," I replied. "I wonder how many beers those old fellows felt like when they got back from the Ruhr".